Imprints 12

VOLUME I

Short Stories
Poetry

Lori Farren
David Friend
Jim Robson
Dom Saliani

CONSULTANT
Ann Manson

EDITORIAL TEAM
Joe Banel
Sandra McTavish
Diane Robitaille
Cathy Zerbst

gagelearning

Permissions Editor: Elizabeth Long
Photo Research: Patricia Buckley
Design, Art Direction, & Electronic Assembly: Wycliffe Smith Design, Inc.
Cover Image: J.L. Stanfield/National Geographic/Firstlight.ca

National Library of Canada cataloguing in publication data

Main entry under title:

Imprints 12

For use in grade 12.
Issued also in hardcover vol.
Contents: v. 1. Short stories, poetry [compiled by Lori Farren, Jim Robson, Dom Saliani
ISBN 0-7715-0948-0

1. Readers (Secondary). I. Farren, Lori.

PE1121.I537 2002a   428.6   C2001-903083-5

We acknowledge the financial support of the Government of Canada through the Book Publishing Industry Development Program for our publishing activities.

ISBN 0-7715-0948-0
2 3 4 5 FP 13 12 11 10
Printed and bound in Canada

The selections collected in *Imprints* are drawn from a wide variety of sources. To respect the integrity of these sources, Gage has preserved the original spelling, grammar, and punctuation used by each author. Gage editorial style, however, is used throughout for activities and other text generated by Gage writers.

Table of Contents

Short Stories

Poetry

Alternate Table of Contents

Short Stories

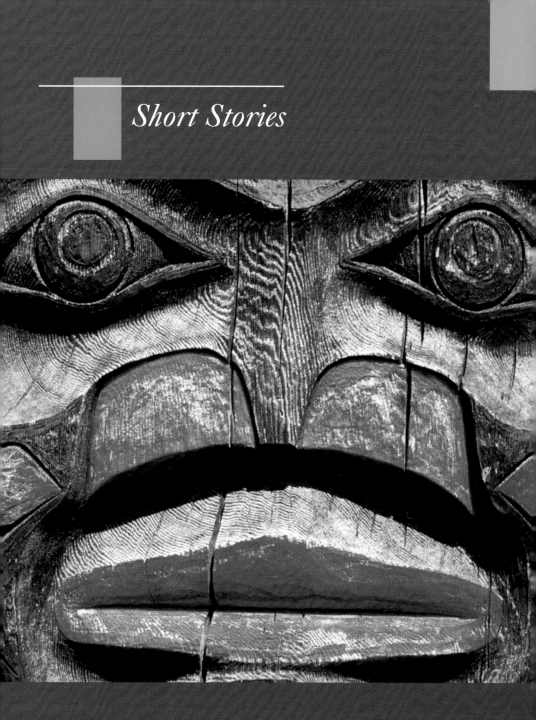

The universe is made of stories, not of atoms.

Muriel Rukeyser

Imagine what a marriage
proposal looks like in a society
where women rule.

Groom Service

by Michael Dorris

1

"She's a piece of pure quartz," Bernard's mother, Martha, said
to Marie's mother, Blanche. "A one-in-a-million that you find
after walking the beach for half your life with your eyes on the
ground. If I had a child like that I would keep her in a safe
place."

Blanche paused her blade midway down the side of the fish
she was scaling. Her face betrayed no expression except exer-
tion, and even in this intermission her teeth remained set, flex-
ing her jaw. The trader steel reflected what little light filtered
through the planks of the smokehouse, and the confined air still
smelled green. Blanche had hewn the boards with a mallet and
chisel in May, as soon as the ground firmed from the spring
runoff, and it took a while before the scent of fire crowded that
of drying wood. With her broad thumb she flicked a piece of fin
off the carved knife handle, then continued her motion.

Martha waited. She had all the time it took.

"You don't know," said Blanche. She shook her head as if
its secrets rolled like line-weights from side to side. She drew a
heavy breath. "You can't imagine. You with such a boy."

Martha sat straighter, all ears, while her hands continued to
explore, repairing the tears on the net that lay across her lap
and hid her pants and boots. Her fingers moved automatically,
finding holes, locating the ends of broken cord and twisting
them into square knots. She kept her nails sharp and jagged,
and when they weren't enough, she bowed her head and bit off
any useless pieces. This was mindless work, the labor of ten
thousand days, and could be done as easily in the dark as in the
light. It required no involvement. Her thoughts were elsewhere.

"You mean Bernard?" Her voice was wary. She had three sons and needed to be sure she knew the one Blanche had in mind.

"Ber-*nard*," Blanche nodded, giving the knife a last run, then inspecting the fish closely before tossing it into the large basket at her feet. The water slopped onto the floor and, from there, leaked to the shale ground inches below. Blanche arched her back and massaged her spine with her fist. With her other hand she reached for the cup of cooled tea that she had nursed for the past half-hour. Martha let the net rest and joined her.

"People talk about him, you know," Blanche said. "His looks, that goes without saying, but the other things too. The respect he pays the old folks. His singing. His calmness. His hunting skill. You must be proud."

Martha closed her eyes as if in great pain. "He is my punishment," she confessed, "but I don't know what I could have done so terrible as to deserve him. He stays out until morning. His hair is always tangled. I sometimes think that the game he brings home has died before he found it, the meat is so tough. You must have him confused with another boy. Or perhaps, with a girl like Marie, you find it hard to think ill of any child."

"Now you make fun of me," Blanche said. "It is well known that Marie has turned out badly. She is lazy and disrespectful, conceited and stubborn. I try my best to teach her, and so do my sisters and even my mother, but she folds her arms and stares at nothing. Hopeless. And she will never find a husband. A boy's mother would have to be desperate to send her son courting at my house."

"But not as desperate as a mother who could tolerate the thought of Bernard as a son-in-law," Martha said. "That would be true desperation. I will never be free of him. I will grow old with him at my side, and with no granddaughters or grandsons to comfort me."

"If only someone like your Bernard would find an interest in Marie," Blanche said as if she had not heard Martha. "If only some young man exactly like him would consent to live in my house, how I would welcome him. I would treat him as my own blood."

The two women met each other's gaze at last. Each held a cup to her lips, and after a few seconds, each drank. Each replaced her cup on the table between them. Each held her mouth firm. Blanche found her knife and reached for a new fish, cool and slippery as a stone over which much water has rushed. Martha shifted the net in her lap, moving a new section to the center. The smell of salt rose like steam as her hands went to work.

"I will speak to him," Martha said.

"And I to her," Blanche replied. "But I know her answer already. I have seen how she regards him."

"She will not be disappointed." Martha allowed one wave of pride to crest. "He's not so bad."

Blanche glanced up at Martha, then looked quickly back to her work. Bernard must be good indeed, she thought, if Martha could not better contain herself.

2

Bernard was drawing with charcoal on a piece of driftwood when his mother returned home. He was twenty-two, lean, and had large teeth. His eyes were dark beneath unusually thick brows, and his hands were long and broad. At the sound of Martha's step, he jumped to his feet and assumed the air of a person about to do something important. His fingers curved as if to hold a tool or a weapon and his eyes narrowed as if to see something far away. He was busy at nothing, his energy humming, ready for a focus. But for once she made no comment about his sloth. She did not despair at the time he wasted scratching on any smooth surface. She did not inspect his sketch and then toss it into the cooking fire. In fact, this afternoon she dealt with him rather mildly.

"Well, it's arranged," she announced. "I spent an endless morning with your future mother-in-law and before I left she had agreed to let you come to see Marie. Don't think it was easy."

Bernard's eyes followed his mother's movements as she crossed the floor and sat in exhaustion on the bed. She pushed off her boots, still caked with beach mud, and rubbed her feet together. She wore no socks.

"Marie?" he said at last. "She's too young. You should have asked me first."

Martha's glare clapped a hand over his mouth. In a moment, Bernard tried again.

"I know they're a good family. I know you want to do right for me. But you could ... *we* could have discussed this. I mean, I think of her as a little girl, not a wife." The word, a stranger on Bernard's tongue, vibrated in the air.

"Stop whining." Martha lost patience. "Who do you 'think of' as a wife? *Doris?*"

Bernard blushed. He wasn't surprised that his mother knew about him and Doris, but it did not seem fair for her to mention it. Doris was a widow whose name brought nervous laughs to teenage boys and smiles of disapproval to everyone else. She was a woman almost twice

Bernard's age with a missing front tooth and eyes that sparked in his memory, a woman who had summoned him for an errand six months ago and whom he now loved better than he would have thought possible. But it was true: he had never thought of Doris as a wife.

"You should see yourself," Martha said. "Keep that face and you won't have to worry about marrying anyone. But don't expect me to support you forever." She noticed the driftwood, still on the floor, and nudged it with her toe to get a better view. Bernard had outlined the mountain across the bay from the village, and tucked a large sun behind its peak. When he drew it he thought it was his best work, but now its lines looked smudged and shaky. Martha leaned forward to pick it up and turn it over, as if expecting another illustration on the back. Finding none, she held it out for Bernard to take.

"Give this to your Doris," she said. "It looks like her under the blanket where she spends her time."

Bernard didn't move, but he watched the wood until his mother let it fall to the floor. He was angry at the shame he felt. He was angry that he knew it was just a matter of time until he would have to call on Marie. He was angry that his mother was right: his mountain *did* look like Doris, turned on her side.

3

When Blanche went into the house and told Marie that their problems were over, that Bernard, the catch of the village, would be courting, she expected some reaction, but her daughter simply folded her arms and stared at the fire.

"Don't you hear me?" Blanche demanded. "Bernard. Coming to see you. Can't you be happy? Can't you say something?"

Marie, however, only rolled her eyes and drummed her fingers against the pine bench upon which she sat. She wore a close-knit woven cap that, in combination with her unfortunately weak chin, made her head resemble an acorn. She was fifteen, just out of her confinement, trained for adulthood to the limits of Blanche and her sister's patience, but still a sulking child. At length she drew up her knees, circled them with her arms, and watched her mother from the corner of her eye.

> A good short story is a work of art which daunts us in proportion to its brevity ... No inspiration is too noble for it; no amount of hard work is too severe for it.
>
> Elizabeth Stuart Phelps

Blanche stood across the long room, talking to her older sister Bonnie. She was not hard to overhear.

"Does she say 'thank you'? Does she appreciate what it means to her, to all of us, to get that damn Martha to agree? Does she care that Bernard could have any girl, from any family?"

Bonnie shook her head sadly. Her surviving children had all been boys and had long since moved to the houses of their wives' families, so she had no experience with reluctant girls, unless, she thought, she counted her memories of Blanche. But that would not do to say, especially not in earshot of Marie, who sat with her head cocked in their direction. Blanche's daughter was the hope of the next generation, the one who had to bring in a husband and produce more daughters than her mother or aunt, if the family was to regain its position. For a moment Bonnie thought of suggesting to Blanche that they present that information to Marie directly, to drop the shadows and point out both her responsibility and her power, but then she rejected the idea. The girl was impressed enough with herself as it was. Instead, Bonnie sympathized with her sister and cast occasional looks at her niece in hopes of catching on Marie's face a secret, a streak of pleasure.

4

"What am I supposed to do?" Bernard asked the next time his uncle visited. Bernard had waited for a private moment, and it came when, just before sleep, Theodore had stepped outside to relieve himself. The trees around the village seemed closer at night, taller, like the sides of a box.

From the darkness came rattling sounds of strangulation that Bernard eventually identified as the older man's yawn. When it, and the noise of splashing water, had abated, Theodore spoke. It was clear that he understood Bernard's problem.

"You do whatever they tell you and you hope they're not as bad as they could be," Theodore said. "You don't complain. You don't assume anything. You stay out of the way, because you never know what they're going to find to dislike. You be what they want."

"It's not fair." Bernard leaned against the side of the house and searched the sky. Thin clouds, silver as wet spiderwebs, passed in the night wind.

"That's true, but there are other things in the world besides owning real estate. Your true home will remain here at your mother's, just as it has been for me, but you can't *live* here forever. You need independence, distance, the chance to be a man in a place where you were never a boy.

Once you get yourself established, you'll understand what I mean. Your life is not all indoors. You'll hang around with your brothers-in-law, your uncles, your friends. Spend time at the men's house. Go to the sweat bath and gripe, or listen to the complaints of others and make jokes. In a year all your wife's family will care about is whether or not you bring in your share. By then you'll know what's what."

"But what if I don't get along with Marie?"

"*Do* get along with her. Get along with her mother. Get along with her auntie. But on your own time do what you want. It's not a big price to pay. It's a daughter-poor clan and the one they've picked out for you is going to control everything someday: rich fishing sites, a big house. Behave yourself now and you'll get your reward. It's not like you're marrying a youngest sister with no prospects."

Which was, Bernard knew, what had happened to Theodore. No wonder he was not more sympathetic.

"How do I tell Doris?" Bernard asked. This was something he had struggled with for days.

"Doris! She could have told *you*. It's good news to her. She gets a younger guy, fresh the way she likes them, and no hard feelings between you." Theodore laughed, and put an arm around Bernard's shoulders. "Listen to some advice, from your great-uncle through me to you," he said. "Groom service is the worst part, so make it as short as possible. Convince her family you won't be a pain in the ass to live with. Rule number one: appreciate everything they do. Compliment, compliment, compliment."

"Did you do that?" Bernard asked. "Did my mother's husband do that?"

"Do fish fry in hot grease? But don't take my word for it. Ask Pete. He's your father."

"I'd be embarrassed," Bernard said. "He and I never talk about serious matters. He's not of the clan."

"A man's a man," Theodore said.

5

"This is what you do," Martha instructed.

It was not yet light and she had awakened Bernard from a sound sleep. He blew into a cup of hot tea as he listened, let the darkness hide the resentment in his face.

"You go hunting and you catch something *good*, I don't care what. Something a little unusual. A beaver, maybe, or a goose. *Not* something small and easy. *Not* a squirrel. *Not* fish. You bring it home and I'll help you clean it. You leave a portion for me as if that's what you always do, to help provide for your family, but you take the best part and you set yourself in front of Blanche's door. You only speak if you're spoken to. You wait for *them* to ask *you*. And if they don't, which they won't right away, you act unconcerned. You do this every day until they invite you in, and then I'll tell you what to do next. This is your chance, so don't ruin it. Now move."

Bernard stepped out into the chill morning grayness, thought briefly of visiting Doris before he went hunting, but then abandoned the idea. He had heard through his mother's husband that Doris had made friends with a seventeen-year-old boy named James.

The dew from high grass had soaked through to Bernard's feet before he reached the edge of the woods. He realized his mother had forgotten to feed him breakfast, forgotten to make him a lunch. He heard a duck call from the lake and paused, but then continued on. He could hear his mother in his mind, and she said a duck wouldn't do.

6

"He's *there*!" Bonnie dropped the firewood she was carrying and rushed to Blanche's side.

Her sister was stirring a pot on the fire, as if what it contained were all that concerned her. "I have eyes," Blanche said. "Keep your voice down. He'll hear you."

"Did you see what he had?" Bonnie asked. "I got a glimpse of something flat and dark, but I didn't want him to catch me looking."

"I think it was a beaver tail. Would you believe, he had the nerve to hold it up to me and smile the first time I passed."

"No!"

"I thought he was better trained. It simply means he'll have to wait longer."

"Did Marie see him yet?"

"She won't go outside." Both sisters turned to the gloom in the rear of the room where Marie crouched, her head lowered over a stick game. Her long hair was loose and covered her shoulders like a shawl, her back to the doorway.

7

"Well, what happened?" Martha demanded when Bernard returned home late in the evening.

"Nothing happened," Bernard said, and threw himself down on his blankets. He raised an arm to cover his eyes, then turned to face the wall.

Martha spotted the sack her son had dropped on the floor and looked inside. The beaver tail and quarters were exactly as she had cleaned them that afternoon, and she took them out to add to the broth she had prepared.

"At least we'll eat well for a while," she said.

"I'm not hungry," Bernard replied, but his mother ignored him.

"Tell me everything."

"There's nothing to tell. I walked over there, dressed like I was going to a feast, carrying that beaver. I trapped it clean, surprised it so completely, there wasn't even adrenaline in its flesh. I thought they'd taste it, invite me to supper, but they walked by me like I wasn't there, their noses in the air."

"Whose noses?" Martha wanted to know.

"The mother and the aunt."

"Not the girl?"

"I saw no girl. I heard no girl."

"Ah," said Martha. "So she's shy. Good."

"Why good?"

"Because then she won't bully you at first, stupid boy. I've seen what happens to the husbands of the bold ones."

The smell of stewing meat filled the room, warm, rich, brown. Martha's husband Pete came into the house at the scent, tipped his head in his son's direction, and asked, "Hard day?"

8

For a week, then two weeks, the same pattern was repeated. Only the animals changed: they ranged from a porcupine to a hind quarter of caribou, from a fat grouse on a bad day to a string of matched silver salmon on a good one. Once Bernard thought he saw a black bear dive into the brush at the side of a stream, but he was momentarily afraid to investigate, and later berated himself. With a bear skin, he thought too late, he would have been irresistible and his long afternoons and evenings at Blanche's closed door would have been over.

As a month passed, Bernard gave up hope. He lost the alertness he had once felt when Blanche or Bonnie or Marie, the most unsympathetic of them all, approached, and he soon tired of the commiseration that Blanche's and Bonnie's husbands cast in his direction as they went about their business. They could remember, their expressions said, what it was like to wait outside this house, but there was nothing they could do. A word from them might slow the process rather than speed it up, might do more damage than good. If boredom was patience, Bernard achieved patience. If learning to exist without expectation of fulfillment was maturity, Bernard matured. At first he used his time to remember Doris, to wonder what she was doing and to regret not doing it with her. Later he thought about hunting, how he could have succeeded the times he had failed, how the animals behaved, how they smelled and sounded. Finally he found himself thinking about Pete, his father, in different ways than he ever had before. In Bernard's mind Pete became more than just his mother's husband; he became another man, an earlier version of Bernard, a fellow sufferer. It had not previously occurred to Bernard how hard it was to be forever a stranger in the house where you lived, to be always a half-visitor. He wondered how Pete stayed so cheerful, and wondered if his grandmother had kept his father waiting long at the doorway before inviting him inside. On an afternoon late in the second week, Bernard had a thought so profound, so unprecedented, that it straightened his back. What if, he wondered, his grandmother had not let Pete in at all? What if Pete had been judged inadequate? Where would that have left Bernard?

The next morning when he went hunting, Bernard returned to the place where he had seen the bear, hid himself behind a log, and waited.

9

"Did you hear?" Pete asked Theodore as they walked the trail from the sweat bath to their wives' houses.

"About Bernard's bear?"

"It must have weighed three hundred pounds. I didn't know Bernard had it in him."

"Have you forgotten what sitting in front of a house will drive you to? What did you catch to get inside Blanche's?"

"Nothing," Pete said. "It was me she couldn't resist."

"You forget," Theodore replied. "I was still a boy in that house. I recall their words of you. Let me see ... I seem to remember some mention of the small size of certain of your parts."

"Poor brother-in-law," Pete said. "You still don't realize the lengths to which they went to avoid hurting your feelings! And how *is* your wife? How is the health of her many elder sisters? Is it true that they become stronger and more robust with every year?"

10

On the second day of the fifth week, just as she passed through the door, Blanche reached down her right hand and snagged one of the bear claws that rested in the basket by Bernard's leg. So quick was her movement, so apparently disconnected to the intent of her mind, so complete her distraction, that Bernard had to look twice to make sure it was gone. All the same, he felt a warm flush spread beneath the skin of his neck, and a feeling of inordinate pride suffused him so thoroughly that he had difficulty remaining still. He had been found worthy, and now it was only a matter of time.

Every day, with more pause and deliberation, Blanche browsed through his offerings and always selected some choice token. Her expression betrayed no gratitude, yet Bernard was sure that occasionally she was pleasantly surprised. Afraid to unbalance their precarious arrangement, he sat still as a listening hare in her presence. He kept his eyes lowered and held his breath until she had departed, but remained ever watchful for any cue that his probation had progressed. At last it came.

"Bernard!" Blanche said one day. She stood in the doorway, her hands on her hips, her head cocked to the side in amazement. "Is that you crouching there so quietly? Please, come in and share our supper, poor as it is. What a pleasure to see you."

Bernard rose slowly, stiff in his joints and half-skeptical that this was some joke, some new test, but when he entered the house, Blanche's hospitality continued and was joined by that of Bonnie, who sat by the fire trimming her husband's hair with a squeaking scissors. "Sit, sit," she motioned to a bench near the door. "What a shy boy you are. Luckily we have some nice moose to feed you."

Indeed they did. Bernard recognized the remains of the foreleg he had offered yesterday. Bonnie passed him a plate with a small portion of tough gristle, gray and cooled. He knew what to say.

"This is wonderful," he exclaimed. "The best I've ever tasted. What cooks you are. But you are too generous. Let me put some back in the pot."

When they refused, politely and with many denials of his compliments, Bernard made a great show of eating. The act of digestion absorbed his total concentration. He rubbed his stomach and cast his eyes to the ceiling in delight. With great subtlety he periodically raised his hand to his mouth, as if to wipe some grease, and used that motion to conceal the small bits of undigestible food he removed from his cheeks and tucked secretly into his pockets.

When he finished, Bernard sat nervously, breathless with anxiety. From the corner of the room he detected a space so devoid of movement that it attracted his attention. He looked, then quickly looked away. Yet his eyes still registered the image of Marie, her hair oiled and braided, wearing a new dress and a necklace made of bear claws, sitting as composed and shaded as a perfect charcoal sketch.

11

"You know, Pete," Martha said as she lay by her husband's side under a robe, "watching Bernard lately brings back memories."

"To me too. Your mother was a terror."

"I notice you still whisper such words, even though she's more than four years gone."

Pete shifted his position and propped on an elbow. In the moonlight Martha's face was seamless and young. A beam like the hottest part of a coal danced off her dark eye. He ran his fingers along her cheek and she turned her head in comfort. "You look the same as then," he said.

Martha caught his hand and brought it to her mouth, let it feel the smile.

"I pestered her, you know, to let you in," she said.

"You didn't care."

"I didn't care the day you found the eagle feathers? I didn't care the day you came an hour later than always?"

"It was raining," Pete said. "The ground was soft and I kept sinking to my knees. I couldn't arrive at your door covered in mud."

"I thought you weren't coming. I confronted my mother and told her that her slowness had cost me …"

"Cost you what?" Pete asked, when Martha's silence persisted.

"Enough talk."

12

Marie watched the back of Bernard's head and admired the sleek sheen of his long hair, the play of muscles in his arms at his every movement. During the last month she had studied every part of him so completely that she could create him in her imagination whenever she chose, and lately she chose often. She had to fight not to laugh when they gave him the worst meat and he had to spit into his hand and act as though it were delicious. She watched the way his fingers held the plate, the way he sat so compact and attentive. She waited for the sound of his soft voice and wondered what he would say when he could speak in private. She made a game of observing his eyes until just the second before they turned to her, and believed she had been discovered only once.

13

Bernard ate almost all of his meals at Blanche's house now, and gradually became more relaxed. For one thing, his distribution increased in both quality and quantity, and he could now expect a reasonable piece of meat or salmon. For another, Blanche's and Bonnie's husbands had begun to join him on his hunts, to show him places to fish that only members of this household knew. He found he liked these men and began to call them "uncle."

Blanche herself still frightened him, but not all the time. There were moments when he found approval in her gaze, times when some word of hers sounded almost like a joke. Bonnie was warmer, more solicitous of his needs, more delighted at the food he brought, and Bernard regarded her as an ally.

As far as Marie was concerned, he still had no clue to her feelings. Even Pete and Theodore observed that this game was lasting longer than the usual and debated whether something might be wrong. They were full of advice for Bernard, full of ideas of how to please Marie, full of reminders that it was her agreement, more than anyone's, that was necessary. But no matter what Bernard did, Marie would not look at him or give him any sign of encouragement. He grew despondent, lost his appetite, found himself thinking once again of Doris and the ease of their association. Marie seemed totally beyond his reach, the focus of mystery and impossible desire. And so he was unprepared on the night, just before the first frost of winter, when, with shaking hands, Marie herself passed him a plate of food.

"This is for you," she said so softly he could barely hear, and she sat beside him while, slowly and with great emotion, he ate.

14

A year later, while waiting for the birth of Marie's first child, Blanche and Martha passed the time by nibbling strips of dried eel. Martha, who had no love for the oily skin, threw hers into the fire, where it sizzled briefly.

"The midwife predicts a girl," Blanche said. "When she spun the charm above Marie's stomach, it revolved to the left."

"A girl is most rewarding," Martha nodded. "But there is a special satisfaction in raising boys. So often I think of times when Bernard was young, so often I miss him around the house."

Blanche reached for another stick of *baleek* and did not answer. Her silence was immediately noticed, as she knew it would be.

"How is he doing?" Martha asked at last.

"He will learn," Blanche said. "He has potential. It is clear he cares greatly for Marie, and she is patient."

"That is one word for it." Martha tossed a handful of scraps into the flame and watched the light flare and dance. "Of course, Bernard was used to ..." She shifted her weight, cleared her throat. "He had such a *happy* home that I'm sure it has taken some adjusting on his part in new surroundings."

"Yes, he *was* somewhat spoiled. But I think he has a good heart."

"As well he must, to remain loyal to such a chinless girl."

"One only hopes their child will inherit the mother's disposition and not be sulky and resentful of every request."

"One can but pray it will have the father's looks and personality."

A single rope of eel remained on the plate. Both women extended a hand toward it, hesitated, and withdrew. It rested between them as they cleaned their teeth with fine bone picks, carefully wiped their fingers, and when, at the sound of Marie's first muffled protest, they rose together and rushed to her side, it remained behind.

Michael Dorris was born in Kentucky, U.S., in 1945. He graduated from Yale University in 1970, taught at Franconia College, and founded the Native American Studies program at Dartmouth College, where he also taught. His works include the novels *The Crown of Columbus* (with Louise Erdrich), *A Yellow Raft in Blue Water*, and *Cloud Chamber*; a short story collection, *Working Men*; as well as non-fiction, essay collections, and a children's novel.

1. *Response*

a. As a reader, did you feel any connection to the character of Bernard? Did your reaction depend on your gender? Explain.

b. The author does not provide a specific setting for this story. What inferences can you make about where and when the events take place? Does the style of language reinforce the setting, or does it have a different purpose?

c. Describe the ritual of "groom service" outlined in this story. Is there a positive purpose to the ritual? Find specific evidence from the story to support your view. What relevance or message, if any, do you find in the story? Explain.
d. Describe the different relationships in this story and list their characteristics.

2. *Literature Studies* Narrative Structure "Groom Service" is told in sections resembling chapters. Analyse the narrative structure of the story, using a chart to present your findings. The chart should have four columns: Sections, Characters, Plot events, and Purpose of the Section. After you have completed the chart, ask yourself why Dorris may have used this particular structure to tell the story. Identify the narrative point of view and comment on whether it is appropriate for the purpose of the story.

3. *Critical Thinking* This story describes a *gynocentric society* (a society ruled by women) that is *matrilineal* (ancestry is traced through the maternal line). Working in a group, reread the story carefully and generate a list of the important rules and customs of this society. Which people seem to be the most influential? What seem to be the ideal characteristics for women? For men? Are there any aspects of this society that might be applied to our own society? Present your ideas in a brief, well-organized opinion piece. Be sure to support your arguments with solid evidence.

4. *Oral Language* Interior Monologue The character of Marie remains in the background and we learn very little about her. Choosing one of the scenes where Marie is present, write an interior monologue of her thoughts as the events unfold. Establish what you believe to be the tone of voice she would use within her own head. Do you think her true character is similar to or different from the way others perceive her? Read your interior monologue aloud to a small group. Afterward, explain why you characterized her as you did. Assess your delivery, considering how effectively you used voice, tone, volume, expressions, and gestures.

The Shining Houses

by Alice Munro

> "She could try all night and never find any words to stand up to their words, which came at her now invincibly from all sides: *shack, eyesore, filthy, property, value.*"

Mary sat on the back steps of Mrs. Fullerton's house, talking—or really listening—to Mrs. Fullerton, who sold her eggs. She had come in to pay the egg money, on her way to Edith's Debbie's birthday party. Mrs. Fullerton did not pay calls herself and she did not invite them, but, once a business pretext was established, she liked to talk. And Mary found herself exploring her neighbour's life as she had once explored the lives of grandmothers and aunts—by pretending to know less than she did, asking for some story she had heard before; this way, remembered episodes emerged each time with slight differences of content, meaning, colour, yet with a pure reality that usually attaches to things which are at least part legend. She had almost forgotten that there are people whose lives can be seen like this. She did not talk to many old people any more. Most of the people she knew had lives like her own, in which things were not sorted out yet, and it is not certain if this thing, or that, should be taken seriously. Mrs. Fullerton had no doubts or questions of this kind. How was it possible, for instance, not to take seriously the broad blithe back of Mr. Fullerton, disappearing down the road on a summer day, not to return?

"I didn't know that," said Mary. "I always thought Mr. Fullerton was dead."

"He's no more dead than I am," said Mrs. Fullerton, sitting up straight. A bold Plymouth Rock[1] walked across the bottom step and Mary's little boy, Danny, got up to give rather cautious chase. "He's just gone off on his travels, that's what he is. May of gone up north, may of gone to the States, I don't know. But he's not dead. I would of felt it. He's not old neither, you know, not old like I am. He was my second husband, he was younger. I never made any secret of it. I had this place and raised my children and buried my first husband, before ever Mr. Fullerton came upon the scene. Why, one time down in the post office we was standing together by the wicket and I went over to put a letter in the box and left my bag behind me, and Mr. Fullerton turns to go after me and the girl calls to him, she says, here, your mother's left her purse!"

Mary smiled, answering Mrs. Fullerton's high-pitched and not trustful laughter. Mrs. Fullerton was old, as she had said—older than you might think, seeing her hair still fuzzy and black, her clothes slatternly-gay,[2] dime-store brooches pinned to her ravelling sweater. Her eyes showed it, black as plums, with a soft inanimate sheen; things sank into them and they never changed. The life in her face was all in the nose and mouth, which were always twitching, fluttering, drawing tight grimace-lines down her cheeks. When she came around every Friday on her egg deliveries her hair was curled, her blouse held together by a bunch of cotton flowers, her mouth painted, a spidery and ferocious line of red; she would not show herself to her new neighbours in any sad old-womanish disarray.

"Thought I was his mother," she said. "I didn't care. I had a good laugh. But what I was telling you," she said, "a day in summer, he was off work. He had the ladder up and he was picking me the cherries off of my black-cherry tree. I came out to hang my clothes and there was this man I never seen before in my life, taking the pail of cherries my husband hands down to him. Helping himself, too, not backward, he sat down and ate cherries out of my pail. Who's that, I said to my husband, and he says, just a fellow passing. If he's a friend of yours, I said, he's welcome to stay for supper. What are you talking about, he says, I never seen him before. So I never said another thing. Mr. Fullerton went and talked to him, eating my cherries I intended for a pie, but that man would talk to anybody, tramp, Jehovah's Witness, anybody—that didn't need to mean anything."

[1] **Plymouth Rock:** a breed of chicken
[2] **slatternly-gay:** untidily colourful and showy

"And half an hour after that fellow went off," she said, "Mr. Fullerton comes out in his brown jacket and his hat on. I have to meet a man downtown. How long will you be, I said. Oh, not long. So off he goes down the road, walking down to where the old tram went—we was all in the bush then—and something made me look after him. He must be hot in that coat, I said. And that's when I knew he wasn't coming back. Yet I couldn't've expected it, he liked it here. He was talking about putting chinchillas[3] in the back yard. What's in a man's mind even when you're living with him you will never know."

"Was it long ago?" said Mary.

"Twelve years. My boys wanted me to sell then and go and live in rooms. But I said no. I had my hens and a nanny goat too at that time. More or less a pet. I had a pet coon too for a while, used to feed him chewing gum. Well, I said, husbands maybe come and go, but a place you've lived fifty years is something else. Making a joke of it with my family. Besides, I thought, if Mr. Fullerton was to come back, he'd come back here, not knowing where else to go. Of course he'd hardly know where to find me, the way it's changed now. But I always had the idea he might of suffered a loss of memory and it might come back. That has happened.

"I'm not complaining. Sometimes it seems to me about as reasonable a man should go as stay. I don't mind changes, either, that helps out my egg business. But this baby-sitting. All the time one or the other is asking me about baby-sitting. I tell them I got my own house to sit in and I raised my share of children."

Mary, remembering the birthday party, got up and called to her little boy. "I thought I might offer my black cherries for sale next summer," Mrs. Fullerton said. "Come and pick your own and they're fifty cents a box. I can't risk my old bones up a ladder no more."

"That's too much," Mary said, smiling. "They're cheaper than that at the supermarket." Mrs. Fullerton already hated the supermarket for lowering the price of eggs. Mary shook out her last cigarette and left it with her, saying she had another package in her purse. Mrs. Fullerton was fond of a cigarette but would not accept one unless you took her by surprise. Baby-sitting would pay for them, Mary thought. At the same time she was rather pleased with Mrs. Fullerton for being so unaccommodating. When Mary came out of this place, she always felt as if she were passing through barricades. The house and its surroundings were so self-sufficient, with their complicated and seemingly unalterable layout of vegetables and flower beds, apple and cherry trees, wired

---

[3]**chinchillas:** a squirrel-like rodent raised for its fur

chicken-run, berry patch and wooden walks, woodpile, a great many roughly built dark little sheds, for hens or rabbits or a goat. Here was no open or straightforward plan, no order that an outsider could under-stand; yet what was haphazard time had made final. The place had become fixed, impregnable, all its accumulations necessary, until it seemed that even the washtubs, mops, couch springs and stacks of old police magazines on the back porch were there to stay.

Mary and Danny walked down the road that had been called, in Mrs. Fullerton's time, Wicks Road, but was now marked on the maps of the subdivision as Heather Drive. The name of the subdivision was Garden Place, and its streets were named for flowers. On either side of the road the earth was raw; the ditches were running full. Planks were laid across the open ditches, planks approached the doors of the newest houses. The new, white and shining houses, set side by side in long rows in the wound of the earth. She always thought of them as white houses, though of course they were not entirely white. They were stucco and siding, and only the stucco was white; the siding was painted in shades of blue, pink, green and yellow, all fresh and vivid colours. Last year, just at this time, in March, the bulldozers had come in to clear away the brush and second-growth and great trees of the mountain forest; in a little while the houses were going up among the boulders, the huge torn stumps, the unimaginable upheavals of that earth. The houses were frail at first, skeletons of new wood standing up in the dusk of the cold spring days. But the roofs went on, black and green, blue and red, and the stucco, the siding; the windows were put in, and plastered with signs that said, Murry's Glass, French's Hard-wood Floors; it could be seen that the houses were real. People who would live in them came out and tramped around in the mud on Sun-days. They were for people like Mary and her husband and their child, with not much money but expectations of more; Garden Place was already put down, in the minds of people who understood addresses, as less luxurious than Pine Hills but more desirable than Wellington Park. The bathrooms were beautiful, with three-part mirrors, ceramic tile, and coloured plumbing. The cupboards in the kitchen were light birch or mahogany, and there were copper lighting fixtures there and in the dining ells. Brick planters, matching the fireplaces, separated the living rooms and halls. The rooms were all large and light and the basements dry, and all this soundness and excellence seemed to be clearly, proudly indicated on the face of each house—those ingenuously similar houses that looked calmly out at each other, all the way down the street.

Today, since it was Saturday, all the men were out working around their houses. They were digging drainage ditches and making rockeries and clearing off and burning torn branches and brush. They worked with competitive violence and energy, all this being new to them; they were not men who made their livings by physical work. All day Saturday and Sunday they worked like this, so that in a year or two there should be green terraces, rock walls, shapely flower beds and ornamental shrubs. The earth must be heavy to dig now; it had been raining last night and this morning. But the day was brightening; the clouds had broken, revealing a long thin triangle of sky, its blue still cold and delicate, a winter colour. Behind the houses on one side of the road were pine trees, their ponderous symmetry not much stirred by any wind. These were to be cut down any day now, to make room for a shopping centre, which had been promised when the houses were sold.

And under the structure of this new subdivision, there was still something else to be seen; that was the old city, the old wilderness city that had lain on the side of the mountain. It had to be called a city because there were tramlines running into the woods, the houses had numbers and there were all the public buildings of a city, down by the water. But houses like Mrs. Fullerton's had been separated from each other by uncut forest and a jungle of wild blackberry and salmonberry bushes; these surviving houses, with thick smoke coming out of their chimneys, walls unpainted and patched and showing different degrees of age and darkening, rough sheds and stacked wood and compost heaps and grey board fences around them—these appeared every so often among the large new houses of Mimosa and Marigold and Heather Drive—dark, enclosed, expressing something like savagery in their disorder and the steep, unmatched angles of roofs and lean-tos; not possible on these streets, but there.

"What are they saying?" said Edith, putting on more coffee. She was surrounded in her kitchen by the ruins of the birthday party—cake and molded jellies and cookies with animal faces. A balloon rolled under-foot. The children had been fed, had posed for flash cameras and endured the birthday games; now they were playing in the back bed-rooms and the basement, while their parents had coffee. "What are they saying in there?" said Edith.

Words set things in motion. I've seen them doing it.
Words set up atmospheres, electrical fields, charges.

Toni Cade Bambara

"I wasn't listening," Mary said, holding the empty cream pitcher in her hand. She went to the sink window. The rent in the clouds had been torn wide open and the sun was shining. The house seemed too hot.

"Mrs. Fullerton's house," said Edith, hurrying back to the living-room. Mary knew what they were talking about. Her neighbours' conversation, otherwise not troubling, might at any moment snag itself on this subject and eddy menacingly in familiar circles of complaint, causing her to look despairingly out of windows, or down into her lap, trying to find some wonderful explanatory word to bring it to a stop; she did not succeed. She had to go back; they were waiting for cream.

A dozen neighbourhood women sat around the living room, absently holding the balloons they had been given by their children. Because the children on the street were so young, and also because any gathering-together of the people who lived there was considered a healthy thing in itself, most birthday parties were attended by mothers as well as children. Women who saw each other every day met now in earrings, nylons and skirts, with their hair fixed and faces applied. Some of the men were there too—Steve, who was Edith's husband, and others he had invited in for beer; they were all in their work clothes. The subject just introduced was one of the few on which male and female interest came together.

"I tell you what I'd do if I was next door to it," Steve said, beaming good-naturedly in expectation of laughter. "I'd send my kids over there to play with matches."

"Oh, funny," Edith said. "It's past joking. You joke, I try to do something. I even phoned the Municipal Hall."

"What did they say?" said Mary Lou Ross.

"Well, *I* said couldn't they get her to paint it, at least, or pull down some of the shacks, and they said no they couldn't. I said I thought there must be some kind of ordinance applied to people like that and they said they knew how I *felt* and they were very *sorry*—"

"But no?"

"But no."

"But what about the chickens, I thought—"

"Oh, they wouldn't let you or me keep chickens, but she has some special dispensation about that too, I forgot how it goes."

"I'm going to stop buying them," Janie Inger said. "The supermarket's cheaper and who cares that much about fresh? And my God, the smell. I said to Carl I knew we were coming to the sticks but I somehow didn't picture us next door to a barnyard."

"Across the street is worse than next door. It makes me wonder why we ever bothered with a picture window, whenever anybody comes to see us I want to draw the drapes so they won't see what's across from us."

"Okay, okay," Steve said, cutting heavily through these female voices. "What Carl and I started out to tell you was that, if we can work this lane deal, she has got to go. It's simple and it's legal. That's the beauty of it."

"What lane deal?"

"We are getting to that. Carl and I been cooking this for a couple of weeks, but we didn't like to say anything in case it didn't work out. Take it, Carl."

"Well, she's on the lane allowance, that's all," Carl said. He was a real estate salesman, stocky, earnest, successful. "I had an idea it might be that way, so I went down to the Municipal Hall and looked it up."

"What does that mean, dear?" said Janie, casual, wifely.

"This is it," Carl said. "There's an allowance for a lane, there always has been, the idea being if the area ever got built up they would put a lane through. But they never thought that would happen, people just built where they liked. She's got part of her house and half a dozen shacks sitting right where the lane has to go through. So what we do now, we get the municipality to put through a lane. We need a lane anyway. Then she has to get out. It's the law."

"It's the law," said Steve, radiating admiration. "What a smart boy. These real estate operators are smart boys."

"Does she get anything?" said Mary Lou. "I'm sick of looking at it and all but I don't want to see anybody in the poorhouse."

"Oh, she'll get paid. More than it's worth. Look, it's to her advantage. She'll get paid for it, and she couldn't sell it, she couldn't give it away."

Mary set her coffee cup down before she spoke and hoped her voice would sound all right, not emotional or scared. "But remember she's been here a long time," she said. "She was here before most of us were born." She was trying desperately to think of other words, words more sound and reasonable than these; she could not expose to this positive tide any notion that they might think flimsy and romantic, or she would destroy her argument. But she had no argument. She could try all night and never find any words to stand up to their words, which came at her now invincibly from all sides: *shack, eyesore, filthy, property, value.*

"Do you honestly think that people who let their property get so rundown have that much claim to our consideration?" Janie said, feeling her husband's plan was being attacked.

"She's been here forty years, now we're here," Carl said. "So it goes. And whether you realize it or not, just standing there that house is bringing down the resale value of every house on this street. I'm in the business, I know."

And these were joined by other voices; it did not matter much what they said as long as they were full of self-assertion and anger. That was their strength, proof of their adulthood, of themselves and their seriousness. The spirit of anger rose among them, bearing up their young voices, sweeping them together as on a flood of intoxication, and they admired each other in this new behaviour as property-owners as people admire each other for being drunk.

"We might as well get everybody now," Steve said. "Save going around to so many places."

It was supper time, getting dark out. Everybody was preparing to go home, mothers buttoning their children's coats, children clutching, without much delight, their balloons and whistles and paper baskets full of jelly beans. They had stopped fighting, almost stopped noticing each other; the party had disintegrated. The adults too had grown calmer and felt tired.

"Edith! Edith, have you got a pen?"

Edith brought a pen and they spread the petition for the lane, which Carl had drawn up, on the dining-room table, clearing away the paper plates with smears of dried ice cream. People began to sign mechanically as they said goodbye. Steve was still scowling slightly; Carl stood with one hand on the paper, businesslike, but proud. Mary knelt on the floor and struggled with Danny's zipper. She got up and put on her own coat, smoothed her hair, put on her gloves and took them off again. When she could not think of anything else to do she walked past the dining-room table on her way to the door. Carl held out the pen.

"I can't sign that," she said. Her face flushed up, at once, her voice was trembling. Steve touched her shoulder.

"What's the matter, honey?"

"I don't think we have the right. We haven't the right."

"Mary, don't you care how things look? You live here too."

"No, I—I don't care." Oh, wasn't it strange, how in your imagination, when you stood up for something, your voice rang, people started, abashed; but in real life they all smiled in rather a special way and you saw that what you had really done was serve yourself up as a conversational delight for the next coffee party.

"Don't worry, Mary, she's got money in the bank," Janie said. "She must have. I asked her to baby-sit for me once and she practically spit in my face. She isn't exactly a charming old lady, you know."

"I know she isn't a charming old lady," Mary said.

Steve's hand still rested on her shoulder. "Hey what do you think we are, a bunch of ogres?"

"Nobody wants to turn her out just for the fun of it," Carl said. "It's unfortunate. We all know that. But we have to think of the community."

"Yes," said Mary. But she put her hands in the pockets of her coat and turned to say thank you to Edith, thank you for the birthday party. It occurred to her that they were right, for themselves, for whatever it was they had to be. And Mrs. Fullerton was old, she had dead eyes, nothing could touch her. Mary went out and walked with Danny up the street. She saw the curtains being drawn across the living-room windows; cascades of flowers, of leaves, of geometrical designs, shut off these rooms from the night. Outside it was quite dark, the white houses were growing dim, the clouds breaking and breaking, and smoke blowing from Mrs. Fullerton's chimney. The pattern of Garden Place, so assertive in the daytime, seemed to shrink at night into the raw black mountainside.

Reservoir by Michael Berger. Digital watercolour

Berger's image is strongly geometrical; identify the basic shapes he uses to construct this landscape. Are there any details in the image that work against its linearity? In a group, discuss the effect the work creates and the ideas the artist might be suggesting.

The voices in the living room have blown away, Mary thought. If they would blow away and their plans be forgotten, if one thing could be left alone. But these are people who win, and they are good people; they want homes for their children, they help each other when there is trouble, they plan a community—saying that word as if they found a modern and well-proportioned magic in it, and no possibility anywhere of a mistake.

There is nothing you can do at present but put your hands in your pockets and keep a disaffected heart.

Alice Munro's first collection of short stories, *Dance of the Happy Shades* (from which this story was taken), was published in 1968 and won a Governor General's Award. In 1977, Munro became the first Canadian to win the Canada-Australia Literary Prize. She went on to win two more Governor General's Awards for her collections, *Who Do You Think You Are?* and *The Progress of Love.*

I. *Response*

a. Why is Mary interested in Mrs. Fullerton? How would you describe their conversation at the beginning of the story?

b. What is revealed about Mrs. Fullerton through her reaction to Mr. Fullerton's leaving?

c. Reread the first section of the story and note any examples of foreshadowing you can detect. Compare your findings with those of a classmate.

d. What do you think is the significance of the story's title?

e. "The Shining Houses" portrays an important conflict in a changing community. Summarize that conflict in your own words. To what degree does the story present both sides of the argument? Do you think the author favours one side over the other? Give evidence for your answer.

2. ***Media*** *Human Interest Story* Imagine you are a print or TV journalist working in the community described in "The Shining Houses." A group led by Carl and Janie has taken their plan for the lane to local council. Mrs. Fullerton is fighting the zone change. Create a human interest story about the conflict. Include quotations from, or an interview with, Mary and other residents. You can present your story either as a written article, or orally, as a live broadcast.

3. ***Critical Thinking*** With the growth of urban development in many areas of the country, we, as a society, are frequently asked to balance the desire for expansion with the desire for preservation. Are there examples of this opposition within your community? If you were a member of a town council, what would you want to see done in your area? In a group, create a set of guidelines for managing growth in your own community. If the group cannot reach a consensus, include a dissenting opinion with your guidelines. List those oral and group skills that you think you used effectively in this activity. What skills would you like to develop?

4. ***Focus on Context*** "The Shining Houses" appeared in *Dance of the Happy Shades*, published in 1968. During this time of intense social activism, women's roles were increasingly being scrutinized and critiqued. Examine the characters of Mrs. Fullerton, Mary, and Janie, commenting on the different characteristics and roles each woman represents. How is Mary different from her neighbours? Speculate on Munro's purpose in writing this story and creating these characters. Does understanding the context of the story increase your understanding or appreciation of it? Explain.

Theme Connections

- *"On the Rainy River," a story about societal pressures, Vol. I, p. 70*
- *"I Am a Rock," an ironic song about not needing others, Vol. I, p. 225*
- *"The Love Song of J. Alfred Prufrock," a poem about conformity, Vol. I, p. 240*
- *"Rink Rage," a magazine article about "mob" actions, Vol. II, p. 76*

Transients in Arcadia

by
O. Henry

**New York, circa 1908,
where the elegant Hotel Lotus
offered a dream of luxury
to those who could afford it.**

There is a hotel on Broadway that has escaped discovery by the summer-resort promoters. It is deep and wide and cool. Its rooms are finished in dark oak of a low temperature. Home-made breezes and deep-green shrubbery give it the delights without the inconveniences of the Adirondacks.[1] One can mount its broad staircases or glide dreamily upward in its aërial elevators, attended by guides in brass buttons, with a serene joy that Alpine climbers have never attained. There is a chef in its kitchen who will prepare for you brook trout better than the White Mountains ever served, seafood that would turn Old Point Comfort—"by Gad, sah!"—green with envy, and Maine venison that would melt the official heart of the game warden.

A few have found out this oasis in the July desert of Manhattan. During that month you will see the hotel's reduced array of guests scattered luxuriously about in the cool twilight of its lofty dining-room, gazing at one another across the snowy waste of unoccupied tables, silently congratulatory.

Superfluous, watchful, pneumatically-moving waiters hover near, supplying every want before it is expressed. The temperature is perpetual April. The ceiling is painted in watercolors to counterfeit a summer sky across which delicate clouds drift and do not vanish as those of nature do to our regret.

[1] **Adirondacks:** a mountain range of north-eastern New York state

The pleasing, distant roar of Broadway is transformed in the imagination of the happy guests to the noise of a waterfall filling the woods with its restful sound. At every strange footstep the guests turn an anxious ear, fearful lest their retreat be discovered and invaded by the restless pleasure-seekers who are forever hounding Nature to her deepest lairs.

Thus in the depopulated caravansary the little band of connoisseurs jealously hide themselves during the heated season, enjoying to the uttermost the delights of mountain and seashore that art and skill have gathered and served to them.

In this July came to the hotel one whose card that she sent to the clerk for her name to be registered read "Mme. Héloise D'Arcy Beaumont."

Madame Beaumont was a guest such as the Hotel Lotus loved. She possessed the fine air of the élite, tempered and sweetened by a cordial graciousness that made the hotel employees her slaves. Bellboys fought for the honor of answering her ring; the clerks, but for the question of ownership, would have deeded to her the hotel and its contents; the other guests regarded her as the final touch of feminine exclusiveness and beauty that rendered the entourage perfect.

This super-excellent guest rarely left the hotel. Her habits were consonant with the customs of the discriminating patrons of the Hotel Lotus. To enjoy that delectable hostelry one must forego the city as though it were leagues away. By night a brief excursion to the nearby roofs is in order; but during the torrid day one remains in the umbrageous fastnesses of the Lotus as a trout hangs poised in the pellucid sanctuaries of his favorite pool.

Though alone in the Hotel Lotus, Madame Beaumont preserved the state of a queen whose loneliness was of position only. She breakfasted at ten, a cool, sweet, leisurely, delicate being who glowed softly in the dimness like a jasmine flower in the dusk.

But at dinner was Madame's glory at its height. She wore a gown as beautiful and immaterial as the mist from an unseen cataract in a mountain gorge. The nomenclature[2] of this gown is beyond the guess of the scribe. Always pale-red roses reposed against its lace-garnished front. It was a gown that the head-waiter viewed with respect and met at the door. You thought of Paris when you saw it, and maybe of mysterious countesses, and certainly of Versailles[3] and rapiers and Mrs. Fiske[4] and

[2]**nomenclature:** literally a system of names or terms used in a particular field of science or art; here used playfully to mean designer
[3]**Versailles:** a French palace just outside of Paris
[4]**Mrs. Fiske:** a famous American actor, playwright, and activist

rouge-et-noir.[5] There was an untraceable rumor in the Hotel Lotus that Madame was a cosmopolite, and that she was pulling with her slender white hands certain strings between the nations in the favor of Russia. Being a citizeness of the world's smoothest roads it was small wonder that she was quick to recognize in the refined purlieus of the Hotel Lotus the most desirable spot in America for a restful sojourn during the heat of midsummer.

On the third day of Madame Beaumont's residence in the hotel a young man entered and registered himself as a guest. His clothing—to speak of his points in approved order—was quietly in the mode; his features good and regular; his expression that of a poised and sophisticated man of the world. He informed the clerk that he would remain three or four days, inquired concerning the sailing of European steamships, and sank into the blissful inanition of the nonpareil hotel with the contented air of a traveller in his favorite inn.

The young man—not to question the veracity of the register—was Harold Farrington. He drifted into the exclusive and calm current of life in the Lotus so tactfully and silently that not a ripple alarmed his fellow-seekers after rest. He ate in the Lotus and of its patronym,[6] and was lulled into blissful peace with the other fortunate mariners. In one day he acquired his table and his waiter and the fear lest the panting chasers after repose that kept Broadway warm should pounce upon and destroy this contiguous but covert haven.

After dinner on the next day after the arrival of Harold Farrington Madame Beaumont dropped her handkerchief in passing out. Mr. Farrington recovered and returned it without the effusiveness of a seeker after acquaintance.

Perhaps there was a mystic freemasonry between the discriminating guests of the Lotus. Perhaps they were drawn one to another by the fact of their common good fortune in discovering the acme of summer resorts in a Broadway hotel. Words delicate in courtesy and tentative in departure from formality passed between the two. And, as if in the expedient atmosphere of a real summer resort, an acquaintance grew, flowered and fructified on the spot as does the mystic plant of the conjuror. For a few moments they stood on a balcony upon which the corridor ended, and tossed the feathery ball of conversation.

"One tires of the old resorts," said Madame Beaumont, with a faint but sweet smile. "What is the use to fly to the mountains or the seashore

---

[5]**rouge-et-noir:** game of chance
[6]**He ate in the Lotus and of its patronym:** "he ate of the Lotus"; in Homer's *The Odyssey*, the lotus-eaters lived in a state of drug-induced bliss

to escape noise and dust when the very people that make both follow us there?"

"Even on the ocean," remarked Farrington sadly, "the Philistines[7] be upon you. The most exclusive steamers are getting to be scarcely more than ferry boats. Heaven help us when the summer resorter discovers that the Lotus is further away from Broadway than Thousand Islands or Mackinac."[8]

"I hope our secret will be safe for a week, anyhow," said Madame, with a sigh and a smile. "I do not know where I would go if they should descend upon the dear Lotus. I know of but one place so delightful in summer, and that is the castle of Count Polinski, in the Ural Mountains."

"I hear that Baden-Baden and Cannes are almost deserted this season," said Farrington. "Year by year the old resorts fall in disrepute. Perhaps many others, like ourselves, are seeking out the quiet nooks that are overlooked by the majority."

"I promise myself three days more of this delicious rest," said Madame Beaumont. "On Monday the *Cedric* sails."

Harold Farrington's eyes proclaimed his regret. "I too must leave on Monday," he said, "but I do not go abroad."

Madame Beaumont shrugged one round shoulder in a foreign gesture.

"One cannot hide here forever, charming though it may be. The château has been in preparation for me longer than a month. Those house parties that one must give—what a nuisance! But I shall never forget my week in the Hotel Lotus."

"Nor shall I," said Farrington in a low voice, "and I shall never *forgive* the *Cedric*."

On Sunday evening, three days afterward, the two sat at a little table on the same balcony. A discreet waiter brought ices and small glasses of claret cup.

Madame Beaumont wore the same beautiful evening gown that she had worn each day at dinner. She seemed thoughtful. Near her hand on the table lay a small chatelaine purse. After she had eaten her ice she opened the purse and took out a one-dollar bill.

"Mr. Farrington," she said, with the smile that had won the Hotel Lotus, "I want to tell you something. I'm going to leave before breakfast

[7]**Philistines:** ignorant and uncultured people
[8]**Thousand Islands or Mackinac:** popular holiday spots: The Thousand Islands community is in southeastern Ontario and upstate New York on the St. Lawrence River; "Mackinac" refers to Mackinac Island in Michigan.

in the morning, because I've got to go back to my work. I'm behind the hosiery counter at Casey's Mammoth Store, and my vacation's up at eight o'clock tomorrow. That paper dollar is the last cent I'll see till I draw my eight dollars salary next Saturday night. You're a real gentleman, and you've been good to me, and I wanted to tell you before I went.

"I've been saving up out of my wages for a year just for this vacation. I wanted to spend one week like a lady if I never do another one. I wanted to get up when I please instead of having to crawl out at seven every morning; and I wanted to live on the best and be waited on and ring bells for things just like rich folks do. Now I've done it, and I've had the happiest time I ever expect to have in my life. I'm going back to my work and my little hall bedroom satisfied for another year. I wanted to tell you about it, Mr. Farrington, because I—I thought you kind of liked me, and I—I liked you. But, oh, I couldn't help deceiving you up till now, for it was all just like a fairy tale to me. So I talked about Europe and the things I've read about in other countries, and made you think I was a great lady.

"This dress I've got on—it's the only one I have that's fit to wear— I bought from O'Dowd & Levinsky on the instalment plan.

"Seventy-five dollars is the price, and it was made to measure. I paid $10 down, and they're to collect $1 a week till it's paid for. That'll be about all I have to say, Mr. Farrington, except that my name is Mamie Siviter instead of Madame Beaumont, and I thank you for your attentions. This dollar will pay the instalment due on the dress tomorrow. I guess I'll go up to my room now."

Harold Farrington listened to the recital of the Lotus's loveliest guest with an impassive countenance. When she had concluded he drew a small book like a checkbook from his coat pocket. He wrote upon a blank form in this with a stub of pencil, tore out the leaf, tossed it over to his companion and took up the paper dollar.

"I've got to go to work, too, in the morning," he said, "and I might as well begin now. There's a receipt for the dollar instalment. I've been a collector for O'Dowd & Levinsky for three years. Funny, ain't it, that you and me both had the same idea about spending our vacation? I've always wanted to put up at a swell hotel, and I saved up out of my twenty per, and did it. Say, Mame, how about a trip to Coney Saturday night on the boat—what?"

The face of the pseudo Madame Héloise D'Arcy Beaumont beamed.

"Oh, you bet I'll go, Mr. Farrington. The store closes at twelve on Saturdays. I guess Coney'll be all right even if we did spend a week with the swells."

Below the balcony the sweltering city growled and buzzed in the July night. Inside the Hotel Lotus the tempered, cool shadows reigned, and the solicitous waiter single-footed[9] near the low windows, ready at a nod to serve Madame and her escort.

At the door of the elevator Farrington took his leave, and Madame Beaumont made her last ascent. But before they reached the noiseless cage he said: "Just forget that 'Harold Farrington,' will you? McManus is the name—James McManus. Some call me Jimmy."

"Good-night, Jimmy," said Madame.

---

[9]**single-footed:** walked with a rapid, regular step

O. Henry is the pseudonym of William Sydney Porter, who was born in North Carolina, U.S., in 1862. He worked in Texas as a clerk and bank teller for over ten years, but was charged with embezzling funds from the bank in 1896. Although the amount was minimal, he fled to the Honduras and only returned to Texas when he discovered that his wife was dying. He turned himself in after her death. Porter was released from prison after serving three years of his five-year sentence, and moved to New York City where he began to write full time. During his lifetime, he published ten collections of short stories and, after his death, a further four collections were published.

I. *Response*

a. Use a reference book to discover the appropriateness of the story's title.

b. What was your reaction to the opening paragraphs of the story and the emphasis on description of the setting? What do you think O. Henry was trying to accomplish?

c. How does O. Henry establish Madame Beaumont as a member of high society and therefore an acceptable guest in the Hotel Lotus? To what degree does he use the same techniques with Harold Farrington? Leaving the question of wealth aside, are the two characters portrayed as suitable guests? Explain.

d. Were you surprised by the confessions from Madame Beaumont and Mr. Farrington? Why or why not?

2. ***Vocabulary*** Reread the story and make a list of ten words with which you are unfamiliar, or which you are unused to seeing in print. Provide a definition and at least one synonym for each word. Rewrite three sentences from the story by substituting the synonym for the original word. How does this affect the tone of the sentences?

3. ***Literature Studies*** *Coincidence and Irony* O. Henry's writing often includes coincidences and irony. How does he use these devices in this story? With a partner, prepare a short presentation for the class, illustrating your findings. How would you rate your ability to analyse the literary devices an author uses?

4. ***Language Conventions*** *Register* Why is the **register** of the language so important to the story's effectiveness? Identify the moment when a new language register appears in the narrative. How would you describe each type of register? What effect does each register have on the reader? Given O. Henry's stature as a writer of short stories, do you believe his choice of register was intentional? Why or why not? Analyse the register you have used in a piece of writing, and assess whether it was an effective choice for your audience and purpose. Experiment with using a change in register, as O. Henry has done, to create a particular effect.

Register refers to the level of formality of language. Language can be characterized according to the social context for which it is appropriate. For example, language with a colloquial register might contain slang expressions and unconventional grammar.

5. ***Media*** *Ad* Reread O. Henry's description of the setting in the opening paragraphs. Using these details as background, create an ad campaign for the owners of the Hotel Lotus. The campaign should include ads in at least two media—radio, TV, magazines, or newspapers. Although you should avoid using too many direct quotations from the story, be sure to maintain a sense of the atmosphere of quiet opulence. Prepare your campaign for presentation to the whole class.

My writing is full of lives I might have lived.
—*Joyce Carol Oates*

For five years Kamau had been held as a political prisoner.
What would he find upon his return home?

The Return

by Ngugi wa Thiong'o

The road was long. Whenever he took a step forward, little clouds of dust rose, whirled angrily behind him, and then slowly settled again. But a thin train of dust was left in the air, moving like smoke. He walked on, however, unmindful of the dust and ground under his feet. Yet with every step he seemed more and more conscious of the hardness and apparent animosity of the road. Not that he looked down; on the contrary, he looked straight ahead as if he would, any time now, see a familiar object that would hail him as a friend and tell him that he was near home. But the road stretched on.

He made quick, springing steps, his left hand dangling freely by the side of his once white coat, now torn and worn out. His right hand, bent at the elbow, held onto a string tied to a small bundle on his slightly drooping back. The bundle, well wrapped with a cotton cloth that had once been printed with red flowers now faded out, swung from side to side in harmony with the rhythm of his steps. The bundle held the bitterness and hardships of the years spent in detention camps. Now and then he looked at the sun on its homeward journey. Sometimes he darted quick side-glances at the small hedged strips of land which, with their sickly-looking crops, maize, beans, and peas, appeared much as everything else did—unfriendly. The whole country was dull and seemed weary. To Kamau, this was nothing new. He remembered that, even before the Mau Mau emergency,[1] the over-tilled Gikuyu holdings[2] wore haggard looks in contrast to the sprawling green fields in the settled area.

A path branched to the left. He hesitated for a moment and then made up his mind. For the first time, his eyes brightened a little as he went along the path that would take him down the valley and then to the village. At last home was near and, with that realization, the faraway look of a weary traveller seemed to desert him for a while. The valley

[1]**Mau Mau emergency:** a violent rebellion aimed at ejecting white settlers from colonial Kenya, 1952–56
[2]**Gikuyu holdings:** lands farmed by the Gikuyu people, but controlled at the time by the English colonial government

and the vegetation along it were in deep contrast to the surrounding country. For here green bush and trees thrived. This could only mean one thing: Honia river still flowed. He quickened his steps as if he could scarcely believe this to be true till he had actually set his eyes on the river. It was there; it still flowed. Honia, where so often he had taken a bathe, plunging stark naked into its cool living water, warmed his heart as he watched its serpentine movement round the rocks and heard its slight murmurs. A painful exhilaration passed all over him, and for a moment he longed for those days. He sighed. Perhaps the river would not recognize in his hardened features that same boy to whom the riverside world had meant everything. Yet as he approached Honia, he felt more akin to it than he had felt to anything else since his release.

A group of women were drawing water. He was excited, for he could recognize one or two from his ridge. There was the middle-aged Wanjiku, whose deaf son had been killed by the Security Forces just before he himself was arrested. She had always been a darling of the village, having a smile for everyone and food for all. Would they receive him? Would they give him a "hero's welcome"? He thought so. Had he not always been a favourite all along the Ridge? And had he not fought for the land? He wanted to run and shout: "Here I am. I have come back to you." But he desisted. He was a man.

"Is it well with you?" A few voices responded. The other women, with tired and worn features, looked at him mutely as if his greeting was of no consequence. Why! Had he been so long in the camp? His spirits were damped as he feebly asked: "Do you not remember me?" Again they looked at him. They stared at him with cold, hard looks; like everything else, they seemed to be deliberately refusing to know or own him. It was Wanjiku who at last recognized him. But there was neither warmth nor enthusiasm in her voice as she said, "Oh, is it you, Kamau? We thought you—" She did not continue. Only now he noticed something else—surprise? fear? He could not tell. He saw their quick glances dart at him and he knew for certain that a secret from which he was excluded bound them together.

"Perhaps I am no longer one of them!" he bitterly reflected. But they told him of the new village. The old village of scattered huts spread thinly over the Ridge was no more.

He left them, feeling embittered and cheated. The old village had not even waited for him. And suddenly he felt a strong nostalgia for his old home, friends and surroundings. He thought of his father, mother and—and—he dared not think about her. But for all that, Muthoni, just as she had been in the old days, came back to his mind. His heart beat faster. He felt desire and a warmth thrilled through him. He quickened his step. He forgot the village women as he remembered his wife. He had stayed with her for a mere two weeks; then he had been swept away by the Colonial Forces.[3] Like many others, he had been hurriedly screened and then taken to detention without trial. And all that time he had thought of nothing but the village and his beautiful woman.

The others had been like him. They had talked of nothing but their homes. One day he was working next to another detainee from Muranga.[4] Suddenly the detainee, Njoroge, stopped breaking stones. He sighed heavily. His worn-out eyes had a faraway look.

"What's wrong, man? What's the matter with you?" Kamau asked.

"It is my wife. I left her expecting a baby. I have no idea what has happened to her."

Another detainee put in: "For me, I left my woman with a baby. She had just been delivered. We were all happy. But on the same day, I was arrested …"

And so they went on. All of them longed for one day—the day of their return home. Then life would begin anew.

Kamau himself had left his wife without a child. He had not even finished paying the bride-price. But now he would go, seek work in Nairobi,[5] and pay off the remainder to Muthoni's parents. Life would indeed begin anew. They would have a son and bring him up in their own home. With these prospects before his eyes, he quickened his steps. He wanted to run—no, fly to hasten his return. He was now nearing the top of the hill. He wished he could suddenly meet his brothers and sisters. Would they ask him questions? He would, at any rate, not tell them all: the beating, the screening and the work on roads and in quarries with an askari[6] always nearby ready to kick him if he relaxed. Yes. He had suffered many humiliations, and he had not resisted. Was there any need? But his soul and all the vigour of his manhood had rebelled and bled with rage and bitterness.

One day these wazungu[7] would go!

One day his people would be free! Then, then—he did not know what he would do. However, he bitterly assured himself no one would ever flout his manhood again.

He mounted the hill and then stopped. The whole plain lay below. The new village was before him—rows and rows of compact mud huts,

---

[3]**Colonial Forces:** the army of Kenya's British colonial government
[4]**Muranga:** district of central Kenya
[5]**Nairobi:** capital city of Kenya
[6]**askari:** a guard or soldier
[7]**wazungu:** Europeans, white people

crouching on the plain under the fast-vanishing sun. Dark blue smoke curled upwards from various huts, to form a dark mist that hovered over the village. Beyond, the deep, blood-red sinking sun sent out finger-like streaks of light that thinned outwards and mingled with the grey mist shrouding the distant hills.

In the village, he moved from street to street, meeting new faces. He inquired. He found his home. He stopped at the entrance to the yard and breathed hard and full. This was the moment of his return home. His father sat huddled up on a three-legged stool. He was now very aged and Kamau pitied the old man. But he had been spared—yes, spared to see his son's return—

Donkeys, Lamu, Kenya by Andrew Macara. Oil on canvas

This painting captures a moment in the everyday life of the town of Lamu, Kenya. What adjectives would you choose to describe this scene? Explain how the artist's use of colour is essential to the impression that the painting creates.

"Father!"

The old man did not answer. He just looked at Kamau with strange vacant eyes. Kamau was impatient. He felt annoyed and irritated. Did he not see him? Would he behave like the women Kamau had met at the river?

In the street, naked and half-naked children were playing, throwing dust at one another. The sun had already set and it looked as if there would be moonlight.

"Father, don't you remember me?" Hope was sinking in him. He felt tired. Then he saw his father suddenly start and tremble like a leaf. He saw him stare with unbelieving eyes. Fear was discernible in those eyes. His mother came, and his brothers too. They crowded around him. His aged mother clung to him and sobbed hard.

"I knew my son would come. I knew he was not dead."

"Why, who told you I was dead?"

"That Karanja, son of Njogu."

And then Kamau understood. He understood his trembling father. He understood the women at the river. But one thing puzzled him: he had never been in the same detention camp with Karanja. Anyway he had come back. He wanted now to see Muthoni. Why had she not come out? He wanted to shout, "I have come, Muthoni; I am here." He looked around. His mother understood him. She quickly darted a glance at her man and then simply said:

"Muthoni went away."

Kamau felt something cold settle in his stomach. He looked at the village huts and the dullness of the land. He wanted to ask many questions but he dared not. He could not yet believe that Muthoni had gone. But he knew by the look of the women at the river, by the look of his parents, that she was gone.

"She was a good daughter to us," his mother was explaining. "She waited for you and patiently bore all the ills of the land. Then Karanja came and said that you were dead. Your father believed him. She believed him too and keened for a month. Karanja constantly paid us visits. He was of your Rika,[8] you know. Then she got a child. We could have kept her. But where is the land? Where is the food? Ever since land consolidation,[9] our last security was taken away. We let Karanja go with her. Other women have done worse—gone to town. Only the infirm and the old have been left here."

---

[8]**Rika:** a Gikuyu social grouping similar to a clan

[9]**land consolidation:** redistribution of land, directed by the Kenyan government

He was not listening; the coldness in his stomach slowly changed to bitterness. He felt bitter against all, all the people including his father and mother. They had betrayed him. They had leagued against him, and Karanja had always been his rival. Five years was admittedly not a short time. But why did she go? Why did they allow her to go? He wanted to speak. Yes, speak and denounce everything—the women at the river, the village and the people who dwelt there. But he could not. This bitter thing was choking him.

"You—you gave my own away?" he whispered.

"Listen, child, child—"

The big yellow moon dominated the horizon. He hurried away bitter and blind, and only stopped when he came to the Honia river.

And standing at the bank, he saw not the river, but his hopes dashed on the ground instead. The river moved swiftly, making ceaseless monotonous murmurs. In the forest the crickets and other insects kept up an incessant buzz. And above, the moon shone bright. He tried to remove his coat, and the small bundle he had held on to so firmly fell. It rolled down the bank and before Kamau knew what was happening, it was floating swiftly down the river. For a time he was shocked and wanted to retrieve it. What would he show his—Oh, had he forgotten so soon? His wife had gone. And the little things that had so strangely reminded him of her and that he had guarded all those years, had gone! He did not know why, but somehow he felt relieved. Thoughts of drowning himself dispersed. He began to put on his coat, murmuring to himself, "Why should she have waited for me? Why should all the changes have waited for my return?"

Ngugi wa Thiong'o was born in Kenya in 1938. He received degrees from the Makerere University in Uganda in 1963 and the University of Leeds in England, in 1964. His first novel, *Weep Not, Child*, was published while he was studying in England. After returning to Kenya, he wrote his second novel, *The River Between*. Ngugi's work involves issues such as Kenyan independence and the Mau Mau rebellion of 1952–56. His novel, *Petals of Blood*, led to his imprisonment in 1978. His book, *Detained: A Writer's Prison Diary*, describes his prison experiences, and his later works include the novel *Matigari* and the play *Ngaahika Ndeenda (I Will Marry When I Want)*.

1. Response

a. Make a list of the hopes and fears that are occupying Kamau's mind upon his return to his village. Compare your list with a classmate's and discuss the similarities and differences.

b. At what point in the story did you first suspect that Kamau would face disappointment? What specific details triggered your suspicion?

c. Explain why the women by the Honia river react so coldly toward Kamau.

d. Do you think it was reasonable or unrealistic for Kamau to expect his wife, Muthoni, to wait for him? Why?

e. Reread the ending carefully. What choices does Kamau consider as he stands before the river? Why do you think he is "relieved" to see the end of the "small bundle" of his personal effects? In your own words, summarize the choice Kamau makes at this crucial moment in his life.

2. Literature Studies *Setting* Using specific references from the story, show how Ngugi's careful descriptions of the setting help to create the story's atmosphere and contribute to its meaning. Present your conclusions either orally or in written form; you might also create a visual component to support your presentation.

3. Focus on Context Use your research skills to prepare one or two pages of background information that you think would help a reader better understand "The Return." For example, you might provide details about some or all of the following: the author; Kenyan geography and culture; the historical setting; and the geopolitical issues the story raises.

4. Media *Analysing News Articles* With a partner, examine six news articles—from various newspapers, magazines, or Internet sites—about Africa. What conclusions can you reach about how Africa is represented in the news? How accurate do you think this portrayal is?

Belisa's words could improve dreams or drive away melancholy—or they could pierce like the sharpest daggers.

Two Words

by Isabel Allende

Translated from the Spanish by Margaret Sayers Peden

She went by the name of Belisa Crepusculario,[1] not because she had been baptized with that name or given it by her mother, but because she herself had searched until she found the poetry of 'beauty' and 'twilight' and cloaked herself in it. She made her living selling words. She journeyed through the country from the high cold mountains to the burning coasts, stopping at fairs and in markets where she set up four poles covered by a canvas awning under which she took refuge from the sun and rain to minister to her customers. She did not have to peddle her merchandise because from having wandered far and near, everyone knew who she was. Some people waited for her from one year to the next, and when she appeared in the village with her bundle underneath her arm, they would form a line in front of her stall. Her prices were fair. For five *centavos* she delivered verses from memory; for seven she improved the quality of dreams; for nine she wrote love letters; for twelve she invented insults for irreconcilable enemies. She also sold stories, not fantasies but long, true stories she recited at one telling, never skipping a word. This is how she carried the news from one town to another. People paid her to add a line or two: our son was born; so and so died; our children got married; the crops burned in the field.

---

[1]**Belisa Crepusculario:** In Spanish, *belleza* means *beauty*, and *crepúsculo* means *twilight*.

Wherever she went a small crowd gathered around to listen as she began to speak, and that was how they learned about each other's doings, about distant relatives, about what was going on in the civil war. To anyone who paid her fifty *centavos* in trade, she gave the gift of a secret word to drive away melancholy. It was not the same word for everyone, naturally, because that would have been collective deceit. Each person received his or her own word, with the assurance that no one else would use it that way in this universe or the beyond.

Belisa Crepusculario had been born into a family so poor they did not even have names to give their children. She came into the world and grew up in an inhospitable land where some years the rains became avalanches of water that bore everything away before them and others when not a drop fell from the sky and the sun swelled to fill the horizon and the world became a desert. Until she was twelve, Belisa had no occupation or virtue other than having withstood hunger and the exhaustion of centuries. During one interminable drought, it fell to her to bury four younger brothers and sisters; when she realized that her turn was next, she decided to set out across the plains in the direction of the sea, in hopes that she might trick death along the way. The land was eroded, split with deep cracks, strewn with rocks, fossils of trees and thorny bushes, and skeletons of animals bleached by the sun. From time to time she ran into families who, like her, were heading south, following the mirage of water. Some had begun the march carrying their belongings on their back or in small carts, but they could barely move their own bones, and after a while they had to abandon their possessions. They dragged themselves along painfully, their skin turned to lizard hide and their eyes burned by the reverberating glare. Belisa greeted them with a wave as she passed, but she did not stop, because she had no strength to waste in acts of compassion. Many people fell by the wayside, but she was so stubborn that she survived to cross through that hell and at long last reach the first trickles of water, fine, almost invisible threads that fed spindly vegetation and farther down widened into small streams and marshes.

Belisa Crepusculario saved her life and in the process accidentally discovered writing. In a village near the coast, the wind blew a page of newspaper at her feet. She picked up the brittle yellow paper and stood a long while looking at it, unable to determine its purpose, until curiosity overcame her shyness. She walked over to a man who was washing his horse in the muddy pool where she had quenched her thirst.

"What is this?" she asked.

"The sports page of the newspaper," the man replied, concealing his surprise at her ignorance.

The answer astounded the girl, but she did not want to seem rude so she merely inquired about the significance of the fly tracks scattered across the page.

"Those are words, child. Here it says that Fulgencio Barba knocked out El Negro Tiznao in the third round."

That was the day Belisa Crepusculario found out that words make their way in the world without a master, and that anyone with a little cleverness can appropriate them and do business with them. She made a quick assessment of her situation and concluded that aside from becoming a prostitute or working as a servant in the kitchens of the rich there were few occupations she was qualified for. It seemed to her that selling words would be an honourable alternative. From that moment on, she worked at that profession, and was never tempted by any other. At the beginning, she offered her merchandise unaware that words could be written outside of newspapers. When she learned otherwise, she calculated the infinite possibilities of her trade and with her savings paid a priest twenty *pesos* to teach her to read and write; with her three remaining coins she bought a dictionary. She pored over it from A to Z and then threw it into the sea, because it was not her intention to defraud her customers with packaged words.

One August morning several years later, Belisa Crepusculario was sitting in her tent in the middle of a plaza, surrounded by the uproar of market day, selling legal arguments to an old man who had been trying for sixteen years to get his pension. Suddenly she heard yelling and thudding hoofbeats. She looked up from her writing and saw, first, a cloud of dust, and then a band of horsemen come galloping into the plaza. They were the Colonel's men, sent under orders of El Mulato, a giant known throughout the land for the speed of his knife and his loyalty to his chief. Both the Colonel and El Mulato had spent their lives fighting in the civil war, and their names were ineradicably linked to devastation and calamity. The rebels swept into town like a stampeding herd, wrapped in noise, bathed in sweat, and leaving a hurricane of fear in their trail. Chickens took wing, dogs ran for their lives, women and children scurried out of sight, until the only living soul left in the market was Belisa Crepusculario. She had never seen El Mulato and was surprised to see him walking towards her.

"I'm looking for you," he shouted, pointing his coiled whip at her; even before the words were out, two men rushed her—knocking over her canopy and shattering her inkwell—bound her hand and foot, and threw her like a duffel bag across the rump of El Mulato's mount. Then they thundered off towards the hills.

Hours later, just as Belisa Crepusculario was near death, her heart ground to sand by the pounding of the horse, they stopped, and four strong hands set her down. She tried to stand on her feet and hold her head high, but her strength failed her and she slumped to the ground, sinking into a confused dream. She awakened several hours later to the murmur of night in the camp, but before she had time to sort out the sounds, she opened her eyes and found herself staring into the impatient glare of El Mulato, kneeling beside her.

"Well, woman, at last you have come to," he said. To speed her to her senses, he tipped his canteen and offered her a sip of liquor laced with gunpowder.

She demanded to know the reason for such rough treatment, and El Mulato explained that the Colonel needed her services. He allowed her to splash water on her face, and then led her to the far end of the camp where the most feared man in all the land was lazing in a hammock strung between two trees. She could not see his face, because he lay in the deceptive shadow of the leaves and the indelible shadow of all his years as a bandit, but she imagined from the way his gigantic aide addressed him with such humility that he must have a very menacing expression. She was surprised by the Colonel's voice, as soft and well modulated as a professor's.

"Are you the woman who sells words?" he asked.

"At your service," she stammered, peering into the dark and trying to see him better.

The Colonel stood up, and turned straight towards her. She saw dark skin and the eyes of a ferocious puma, and she knew immediately that she was standing before the loneliest man in the world.

"I want to be President," he announced.

The Colonel was weary of riding across that Godforsaken land, waging useless wars and suffering defeats that no subterfuge could transform into victories. For years he had been sleeping in the open air, bitten by mosquitoes, eating iguanas and snake soup, but those minor inconveniences were not why he wanted to change his destiny. What truly troubled him was the terror he saw in people's eyes. He longed to ride into a town beneath a triumphal arch with bright flags and flowers everywhere; he wanted to be cheered, and be given newly laid eggs and freshly baked bread. Men fled at the sight of him, children trembled, and women miscarried from fright; he had had enough, and so he had decided to become President. El Mulato had suggested that they ride to the capital, gallop up to the Palace and take over the government, the way they had taken so many other things without anyone's permission. The Colonel, however, did not want to be just another tyrant;

there had been enough of those before him and, besides, if he did that, he would never win people's hearts. It was his aspiration to win the popular vote in the December elections.

"To do that, I have to talk like a candidate. Can you sell me the words for a speech?" the Colonel asked Belisa Crepusculario.

She had accepted many assignments, but none like this. She did not dare refuse, fearing that El Mulato would shoot her between the eyes, or worse still, that the Colonel would burst into tears. There was more to it than that, however; she felt the urge to help him because she felt a throbbing warmth beneath her skin, a powerful desire to touch that man, to fondle him, to clasp him in her arms.

All night and a good part of the following day, Belisa Crepusculario searched her repertory for words adequate for a presidential speech, closely watched by El Mulato, who could not take his eyes from her firm wanderer's legs and virginal breasts. She discarded harsh, cold words, words that were too flowery, words worn from abuse, words that offered improbable promises, untruthful and confusing words, until all she had left were words sure to touch the minds of men and women's intuition. Calling upon the knowledge she had purchased from the priest for twenty *pesos*, she wrote the speech on a sheet of paper and then signalled El Mulato to untie the rope that bound her ankles to a tree. He led her once more to the Colonel, and again she felt the throbbing anxiety that had seized her when she first saw him. She handed him the paper and waited while he looked at it, holding it gingerly between thumbs and fingertips.

"What does this say?" he asked finally.

"Don't you know how to read?"

"War's what I know," he replied.

She read the speech aloud. She read it three times, so her client could engrave it on his memory. When she finished, she saw the emotion in the faces of the soldiers who had gathered round to listen, and saw that the Colonel's eyes glittered with enthusiasm, convinced that with those words the presidential chair would be his.

"If after they've heard it three times, the boys are still standing there with their mouths hanging open, it must mean the thing's damn good, Colonel," was El Mulato's approval.

Literature is the human activity that takes the fullest and most precise account of variousness, possibility, complexity, and difficulty.

Lionel Trilling

"All right, woman. How much do I owe you?" the leader asked.

"One *peso*, Colonel."

"That's not much," he said, opening the purse he wore at his belt, heavy with proceeds from the last foray.

"The *peso* entitles you to a bonus. I'm going to give you two secret words," said Belisa Crepusculario.

"What for?"

She explained that for every fifty *centavos* a client paid, she gave him the gift of a word for his exclusive use. The Colonel shrugged. He had no interest at all in her offer, but he did not want to be impolite to someone who had served him so well. She walked slowly to the leather stool where he was sitting, and bent down to give him her gift. The man smelled the scent of a mountain cat issuing from the woman, a fiery heat radiating from her hips, he heard the terrible whisper of her hair, and a breath of sweet mint murmured into his ear the two secret words that were his alone.

"They are yours, Colonel," she said as she stepped back. "You may use them as much as you please."

El Mulato accompanied Belisa to the roadside, his eyes as entreating as a stray dog's, but when he reached out to touch her, he was stopped by an avalanche of words he had never heard before; believing them to be an irrevocable curse, the flame of his desire was extinguished.

During the months of September, October and November, the Colonel delivered his speech so many times that had it not been crafted from glowing and durable words, it would have turned to ash as he spoke. He travelled up and down and across the country, riding into cities with a triumphal air, stopping in even the most forgotten villages where only the dump heap betrayed a human presence, to convince his fellow citizens to vote for him. While he spoke from a platform erected in the middle of the plaza, El Mulato and his men handed out sweets and painted his name on all the walls in gold frost. No one paid the least attention to those advertising ploys; they were dazzled by the clarity of the Colonel's proposals and the poetic lucidity of his arguments, infected by his powerful wish to right the wrongs of history, happy for the first time in their lives. When the Candidate had finished his speech, his soldiers would fire their pistols into the air and set off fire-crackers, and when finally they rode off, they left behind a wake of hope that lingered for days on the air, like the splendid memory of a comet's tail. Soon the Colonel was the favourite. No one had ever witnessed such a phenomenon: a man who surfaced from the civil war, covered with scars and speaking like a professor, a man whose fame spread to every corner of the land and captured the nation's heart. The press focused their attention on him. Newspapermen came from far away to interview him and repeat his phrases, and the number of his followers and enemies continued to grow.

"We're doing great, Colonel," said El Mulato, after twelve successful weeks of campaigning.

But the Candidate did not hear. He was repeating his secret words, as he did more and more obsessively. He said them when he was mellow with nostalgia; he murmured them in his sleep; he carried them with him on horseback; he thought them before delivering his famous speech; and he caught himself savouring them in his leisure time. And every time he thought of those two words, he thought of Belisa Crepusculario, and his senses were inflamed with the memory of her feral scent, her fiery heat, the whisper of her hair and her sweet mint breath in his ear, until he began to go around like a sleepwalker, and his men realized that he might die before he ever sat in the presidential chair.

"What's got hold of you, Colonel?" El Mulato asked so often that finally one day his chief broke down and told him the source of his befuddlement: those two words that were buried like two daggers in his gut.

"Tell me what they are and maybe they'll lose their magic," his faithful aide suggested.

"I can't tell them, they're for me alone," the Colonel replied.

Saddened by watching his chief decline like a man with a death sentence on his head, El Mulato slung his rifle over his shoulder and set out to find Belisa Crepusculario. He followed her trail through all that vast country, until he found her in a village in the far south, sitting under her tent reciting her rosary of news. He planted himself, straddle-legged, before her, weapon in hand.

"You! You're coming with me," he ordered.

She had been waiting. She picked up her inkwell, folded the canvas of her small stall, arranged her shawl around her shoulders, and without a word took her place behind El Mulato's saddle. They did not exchange so much as a word in all the trip; El Mulato's desire for her had turned into rage, and only his fear of her tongue prevented his cutting her to shreds with his whip. Nor was he inclined to tell her that the Colonel was in a fog, and that a spell whispered into his ear had done what years of battle had not been able to do. Three days later they arrived at the encampment, and immediately, in view of all the troops, El Mulato led his prisoner before the Candidate.

"I brought this witch here so you can give her back her words, Colonel," El Mulato said, pointing the barrel of his rifle at the woman's head. "And then she can give you back your manhood."

The Colonel and Belisa Crepusculario stared at each other, measuring one another from a distance. The men knew then that their leader would never undo the witchcraft of those two accursed words, because the whole world could see the voracious puma's eyes soften as the woman walked to him and took his hand in hers.

Isabel Allende was born in Lima, Peru, in 1942. After the fall of her uncle Salvador Allende's government, she moved with her family to Venezuela, where she worked as a journalist. She then lived in the U.S. until her exile ended in 1988. Her first novel, *La casa de los espíritus (The House of the Spirits)*, was made into a motion picture in 1993. Her other works include the novels *De amor y de sombra (Of Love and Shadows)*, *Eva Luna*, *El Plan Infinito (The Infinite Plan)*, and *Hija de la Fortuna (Daughter of Fortune)*; a short story collection; and the non-fiction memoir, *Paula*, about Allende's daughter who died from the genetic disorder porphyria. "Belisa" is an anagram of Isabel.

1. Response

a. "She made her living selling words." In your own words, describe Belisa's occupation. Why did she create this job for herself?

b. What evidence is there that Belisa has a remarkable ability with words? Provide at least three examples. Why is Belisa so popular with the people she travels among?

c. Why do you think Belisa decides to help the Colonel, despite his murderous reputation?

d. Suggest a possible symbolic meaning for the story based on what the two main characters seem to represent. What fundamental conflict(s) does the story convey?

2. **Literature Studies** *Blended Genres* "Two Words" combines the concrete detail of a realistic narrative with the exaggeration and improbability of a folk tale or tall tale. For each of these two aspects of the story, identify several quotations that serve as examples. What is your personal response to this blend of genres? What advantages do you think it offers a writer?

3. **Oral Language** *Group Presentation* In a group, select four or five individual words from the story that you think best describe Belisa. Some words should reflect other characters' views of her, while others should suggest her own perspective. Together, create an imaginative oral presentation that shows these different aspects of Belisa.

4. **Film Study** Assume that "Two Words" has been adapted into a feature-length film and create a storyboard for a movie trailer to represent it. Incorporate details and ideas from the story in your trailer.

5. **Writing** *Journal Entry* From the Colonel's point of view, write a journal entry that explains how Belisa has transformed him. Include the two words she has revealed to him, and the impact they have. Consider how your purpose and the role you have assumed will affect your writing.

> Her profession was words and she believed
> in them deeply. The articulation, interpretation,
> appreciation, and preservation of good words ...
> words could incite, soothe, destroy,
> exorcise, redeem.
>
> —Gail Goodwin

Theme Connections

- *"How Should One Read a Book?" an essay about the power of literature, Vol. II, p. 17*
- *"Making Poetry Pay," an anecdote about the power of words, Vol. II, p. 40*
- *"What Will Your Verse Be?" a movie monologue about the importance of language, Vol. II, p. 270.*

A Marker on the Side of the Boat

"By flashes of the long-range artilleries I could detect no personal shelters on either sidewalk. It was death's ideal coordinates."

by Bao Ninh

Translated from the Vietnamese by Linh Dinh

In my life, I've been here, there, but I've had few chances to visit Hanoi.[1] Once when I was little, once during the war, and a couple times years later. That's why, aside from Turtle Lake and Long Bien Bridge, I can only recall Hang Co Train Station and a street with trolley tracks on it. But in spite of this, when I shut my eyes to peer into the crevices of my memory, I can always conjure up, if only dimly, a general image of its streets. This remote, alien city, with which I have had no intimacy, had, over the years, silently insinuated itself into my consciousness as a beloved place. It is a love born out of nothing, less of an emotion than a light sensation, melancholic, plotless, a souvenir from my war-filled youth, a youth that although long-gone, still reverberates with its echoes. Like the sounds of rain, of wind blowing through a room or of leaves falling, never to be forgotten.

Twenty years have already passed. Hanoi back then and Hanoi today must be as different as sky and earth.

That day, I was driving my division commander from the battle of Quang Tri[2] to a meeting at military headquarters, outside the capital. We arrived to find the city in a state of siege. It was truly a life-and-death battle, a blood struggle which, after

---

[1] **Hanoi:** capital of Vietnam; also capital of North Vietnam from 1954–75
[2] **Quang Tri:** a Vietnamese province; site of a decisive North Vietnamese victory in 1972

twelve days and nights, would change the faces of both winner and loser. In such a dire situation, I did not dare request a leave to visit my village; I only asked for permission to go into the city to deliver a handful of letters given to me by my buddies who were from Hanoi. I wanted to visit each family so I could receive a letter in turn, to bring a little joy back to our soldiers. On Christmas day, I was given permission to go into town, and was told to be back by midnight.

Without knowing the neighborhoods, and with nine letters to deliver, I still wasn't worried. I thought I would find the first address, then ask for directions to go to the next one. I didn't anticipate having to slip each one of those letters under the door. That day, all of Hanoi seemed to have been abandoned.

By the time I had delivered my last letter, the sky was pitch-dark. The long, deserted street lay soaked in rain, punctuated by dim circles of streetlights. I asked for direction to Vong. A militiaman in a frond jacket kindly escorted me for a stretch. At a three-way intersection, before we parted, he pointed to the trolley tracks hugging the sidewalk and said to follow them to get to my destination.

Vietnamese Fleeing on Street, Saigon by unknown photographer.

With my helmet on and my collar up, I plunged into that fine gauze of drizzle. The night was chilly. The tracks were like a trail forging through the jungle of darkened houses. A city during wartime, on a precipice, abandoned. I walked on doggedly, my body numbed. There were endless dark stretches without a single pedestrian or a stall. The night exhaled its cold, wet air, soaking me right down to my empty stomach. My joints felt stiff, aching, as if ready to be jarred apart. A fever that had been simmering all evening crept up my spine. I couldn't stop shivering. My brain slowed down. My knees felt like buckling. I hadn't even walked that far, and already I was counting my steps. Without seeing where I was going, I almost ran into the front of a trolley, a black mass parked in the middle of the street.

I staggered onto the sidewalk and wobbled beneath the eaves of a house. With my back leaning against the door, teeth chattering, I slowly slid down until I was sitting on the wet step, cold as a block of ice. My heart was freezing. I groaned until I could groan no more. My shivering became more violent. My body temperature was at a dangerous level. I thought numbly:

"If I'm not careful this could be the end. Other people stricken with fever die on a hammock in the middle of a jungle. I'll die sitting up, certainly, to be metamorphosed into a rock in front of someone's door."

Above my head, the corrugated tin roof shivered. The wind blew the rain right onto the stoop. Already wet, I got wetter. Dizzy, breathing in gulps, I knew I had to marshal all my energy to get up and continue, but I had no willpower left. It was draining out of me like water from a broken vase. At that point, the door behind me inched open. I heard the noise but could make no sense of it. Unconsciousness, like a letting-go and a sigh of relief, seduced me from my own body ...

Time stopped for I don't know how long. I opened my eyes slowly. My consciousness settled on a rim of light. Still wobbly, uncertain, I nevertheless knew I was indoors, and no longer delirious. The walls appeared to have been painted a pale green, although faded with time. The ceiling was dark. The warm air redolent of camphor.[3] I shifted lightly. The bed creaked beneath my body. I was under a blanket, with my head on a pillow: tranquil, dried, warm, it was unreal. I turned my body. On a night table by the corner of the room, a small oil lamp gave off a dirty yellow light. A clock kept time by monotonously ticking off the seconds. The sudden thought of time startled me; I groaned.

"Oh, Brother ..." Someone's hand caressed my cheek, and a soft, soothing voice whispered, "You've recovered. I was really worried ..."

---

[3]**camphor:** a strong-smelling medicinal compound

My heart froze, then beat wildly. I was embarrassed. What was happening; who was this woman?

"I …" I finally opened my mouth, tongue-tied, stuttering, "Where am I … Where is this?"

"This is my house, Brother." Her soft hand touched my forehead. "You are my guest."

I tried to regain my composure, my strength. Breathing deeply, I turned toward my hostess. She was sitting on the edge of the bed, with her face beyond the lamp's illumination. I could only make out her shoulders and her hair.

"You still have a touch of that fever, Brother, but you've gotten much better, luckily. You scared the hell out of me in the beginning. I was frightened to death."

"I'm in trouble …" I gasped, "It's past time for me to report back. I, I have to go …"

"Oh, Brother, you're in no shape to go anywhere. Outside, in the cold, you'll only get sick again. Besides, your clothes are being hung to dry in the kitchen. You can't wear them yet. They're still damp."

What? I realized what had happened. I quickly touched my thigh and chest, shuddering, wishing I could contract my body. Beneath the quilted blanket, I was practically naked. "I'll bring you some rice gruel from the kitchen, all right?" The woman spoke casually and got up from the bed. "There is a change of clothing by the pillow for you to wear. It's also an Army uniform."

Without taking the oil lamp, she turned and walked out the door into the darkness. I threw the blanket aside and sprang out of bed. The strong aroma of medicinal balm from beneath the blanket stung my eyes. I dressed quickly. The uniform, new, reeking of camphor, was a reasonable fit. Decked out like a soldier again, I seemed to have regained my strength, although my entire body ached, my head was numb, and a ringing lingered in my ears.

As tired as I was, I could detect, immediately, the smell of hot rice gruel as it was being brought into the room by my hostess. She walked softly, her clogs barely making a noise on the wooden floor. She placed the tray on the table and turned up the knob on the oil lamp.

"The rain has stopped," she said, then sighed, for no apparent reason.

In the dimness of that room, I stared silently. This wonderful stranger was like an illusion conjured up in front of my eyes. An unearthly illusion, kind and beautiful. Kind and beautiful, her face, her eyes and lips, although I never really had a chance to look at her. The moment had arrived for this city. Within a fraction of a second, there won't be time for heaven and earth to react, no time to even shudder.

Something monstrous, violent, suddenly stabbed the silence. Out of nowhere, a reconnaissance plane—just one—thunderously slashed its way across the sky, skimming the city's rooftops. Inside the room, even the oil lamp seemed to be holding its breath …

"I think it's gone," she whispered, trembling, a pale smile on her face. "They're just trying to scare us."

"Yes," I said, "Only some spy trying to sneak up on us, don't …"

I was trying to reassure her, to tell her there was nothing to be scared of, when the horrible air siren started wailing, interrupting my sentence. Although I had heard it many times in previous nights and had learned to anticipate the sound, the air siren still made my heart freeze. Never before had this messenger of death reverberated so terrifyingly. The way it howled and screamed—desperate, angry, hysterical—made people want to scream along with it. "B-52s,[4] B-52s, B-52s are coming!" the public speaker frantically blared. "B-52s! Ninety kilometers from Hanoi. Eighty kilometers."

"Those Americans!" I said. "They're coming. That last guy was a scout."

"Yes. It's the B-52s. One more night."

"We'll have to go to the shelter!" I couldn't hide my nervousness. "They're getting near. Quick!"

"But how are you feeling?" She sighed, filled with childish concern. "It's very cold outside."

My premonition of danger suddenly became more palpable. With my mouth dry, my throat contracted, the drum in my chest was banging away. Never before had my intuition deceived me.

"Eat some, Brother, while it's still hot …"

"No!" I said, my voice hoarse, "Hot cold nothing! The bombs are falling soon. They're carpet-bombing[5] us!"

"How do you know?" she blurted in terror.

"I can smell it! Quick! To the shelter!" I practically shouted.

After blowing out the lamp, she grabbed me by the wrist and led me out of the room. My tenseness had been transferred to her. Gasping, her clogs beat a fierce rhythm on the floor. We went down the stairs, then had to pass through a long, narrow, wet corridor before making it to the street. The rain had stopped. The sky had cleared up somewhat. The air was crisp, transparent, eerie. In the middle of the street, right outside the door, the same trolley sullenly sat, like a stranded ship.

---

[4]**B-52s:** long-range bombers used by the U.S. Air Force
[5]**carpet-bombing:** systematic bombing used to devastate a large area

On the sidewalk, the personal shelter, cast out of cement, gaped open its black mouth.

"We should go to the public shelter, Brother," the woman said between quick breaths, "I never want to go inside one of these round ones. There's stagnant water at the bottom. It's gross."

"Now this!" I said, irritated.

"It's only down the street, Brother. Plus, there will be lots of people. It won't be so scary."

We lunged forward into the wind. The entire city was in hiding. In the deadly silence, there were only the two of us, a couple alone in the midst of terror. The seconds ticked by but our escape route seemed endless. A three-way intersection. Then a four-way intersection. The public shelter was nowhere in sight. Wearing those clogs, she couldn't run. But then, oh God, it was already too late to run. Artillery was opening up in the outlying areas. The loud roars of 100-millimeter guns going off in unison. Brilliant flashes. Flame arrows, in pairs, thunderously lunging upward, tearing into the cloud ceiling, leaving red trails behind them. Surrounded by the frantic sounds of our troops' firepower, I could sense what was about to happen in the sky above. I had seen much carnage on the battlefield as a foot soldier. I knew how much chance there is in life-and-death matters. For the two of us, I knew it was over. The bombs were about to fall right on that street.

Fate had wickedly placed us in the middle of a long street with no houses on either side, only high walls running into the distance. By the flashes of the long-range artilleries, I could detect no personal shelters on either sidewalk. It was death's ideal coordinates. A few more hurried steps would not have made a difference.

"They're dropping them!" I said and grabbed her arm.

"Brother, only a little more!"

"We don't have time," I calmly said, with unearthly composure. "The bombs are coming right now. Lie down, quickly, and don't panic."

She obediently lay down next to me, at the foot of a brick wall. She was very confused and only half-believed my deadly pronouncements. But I knew that, within ten seconds or less, the bombs would come. The B-52s, those monstrous dragons, sowers of terror, were no strangers to me. In the South, they would fly at a lower altitude during the day, in formations of three or six planes, arrogantly across the sky, sowing streaks of thick smoke behind them as their bombs rained down. These rains could collapse a side of a mountain, bury a stretch of a river or wipe out an entire forest. But this was no rain; the sky itself was falling. In the place of mountains and forests were houses and streets. The sky was one vast menace, and the city appeared as small as the palm of a hand. In the face of such destruction, I thought, how flimsy is human life. I tensed and waited.

It was as if I didn't hear the explosions. Although I was anticipating the noise, it still took me by surprise. My vision abruptly darkened. The earth shuddered, writhed. Space itself became distorted. Something burning, sharp, slapped me in the face. Heat from the bombs filled my lungs.

She rolled toward me, seeking shelter—her cold body pressing against mine; her breath on my stunned, sweaty face; her hair disheveled.

Another string of bombs came, this time appearing to be right on the other side of the wall. Earth, rocks, cement, roof tiles, houses, all blew up together. The heavens screamed, shattered. Waves of heat rolled across the earth's surface. Die now! Die now! Die..ie..ie. I clutched her, clenching my teeth, waiting for that split second when our bones and flesh would be torn asunder. The bombs came steadily, savagely, howling, exploding one after another. After every explosion, every wave of heat, our bodies coiled more tightly together. The crushing shift in atmospheric pressure left us reeling, stupefied.

Suddenly, death relaxed its claws. The big door in the sky was slammed shut. Silence. The explosion of the last bomb stopped all the others.

We continued to lie still, clutching each other. It was as if we had become paralyzed, incredulous at the fact that we were still alive. We kept in that position for a long time before she wriggled herself free from my grasp.

I slowly helped her to get up. With a shoulder of her shirt torn, her hair disheveled, fear in her eyes, she groped with her feet trying to find her clogs, those useless high-heeled clogs. Billows of thick smoke drifted by. There was a burnt smell of bomb powder in the air. The sky was a bruised red.

As the humming subsided in my ears, I could hear, from somewhere nearby, voices crying for help. The whole neighborhood quickly went into a clamor. A crowd emerged, frantically rushing forward with picks, shovels, crowbars and stretchers.

"Don't just stand there like that!" Someone angrily yelled, his voice hoarse, thick with pain. "The shelter has collapsed. People are dying right in front of you. Oh, God!"

"Oh, my God! I think it's the public shelter. There are so many people in there!" the woman blurted out.

"I'll have to go give them a hand. You go home first. I'll follow!" I said.

I released her hand and ran hastily after the crowd. As I ran, I turned back, motioned with my hand and shouted:

"Go home! Wait there for me!" Near the site of the explosion, before I was to plow into the smoking remnants of the freshly destroyed houses, I turned back one more time. After a hellish night, it was the last glimpse I had of my beloved and illusory figure.

But it shouldn't have been the last time. I should have been able to return to that same house, to the same room where I was the previous night, to see this woman again. It was morning, a long time after the all-clear signals. I followed the trolley tracks, retracing my path from the night before, to go back to her house.

I thought nothing at first when I had to step aside to dodge a trolley. It was cold and the street was empty. The old, rusty trolley lunged forward; the bell silent; its steel wheels shrieking, throwing off sparks; the engine making an ear-shattering racket. But as it passed me, I gave a little start, as if my heart had just been whipped.

The street was straight, endless, without intersections. On each side of the street, the same houses crowded into each other, all identical, monotonous: a gloomy, grouchy façade shaded by a rusty tin roof; three steps leading to a single door. In front of every house was a cement hole. Since the trolley, my only clue, was gone, all I knew for sure was which side of the street the house was on. Everything looked the same, the same uneven, broken sidewalk, with puddles of stagnant water; the same walls and leaky roofs; the same arjun trees and light poles.

Although I had no time to spare, I stalked back and forth on that street, brooding over my failure. I stared into the houses and at the faces of people coming out. By the time another trolley came clanking by, I had to give up. With a face still covered in soot and ash, limbs all scratched, and wearing tatters stained with blotches of blood from the night's victims, I trudged dejectedly along the trolley tracks toward my destination on the outskirts of the city.

After the war, on my rare visits to Hanoi, I would always return to that same street. I would simply walk down it, not to find anything or go anywhere. The last time I got off at Hang Co train station, I could no longer recognize my old street. Hanoi had abolished the trolleys. The streets were glamorous; the houses beautiful; life happy …

There may come a day when people will have a hard time imagining a period when this city went through what I saw twenty years ago, when I was a very young man. ❯

Bao Ninh was born in Hanoi in 1952. In 1969, he served in North Vietnam's Glorious 27th Youth Brigade during the Vietnam War and was one of the ten survivors of the five hundred youths who fought with the brigade. His first novel, *The Sorrow of War*, is a semi-autobiographical work about his war experiences, and has been translated into many languages. Ninh's works have been published in *Granta*; in the U.S. anthology *The Other Side of Heaven: Post-War Fiction by Vietnamese & American Writers*; and in the French anthology *Terres des Éphémères*. The title of this story refers to a folk tale about a fisherman who, to mark the spot where he dropped his sword into a lake, made a mark on the side of his boat.

1. Response

a. Reread the first paragraph of the story. What does it suggest about the narrator's feelings about the city of Hanoi?

b. What do you think is the predominant mood of this story? Select one passage that you think truly captures this mood and give reasons for your choice.

c. Explain the significance of the story's title.

d. Find at least one example of irony in the story. Clarify the nature of the irony to a partner.

e. Explain how the influence of chance or luck is such an important element in this story.

2. Focus on Context

Discuss the background information provided on Bao Ninh with a partner. Speculate on why Ninh wrote this story, and who his original audience was. How does the context in which you read the story—in a Canadian classroom, decades after the war—affect your appreciation of it?

3. **Language Focus** *Descriptive Language* Identify three passages in the story that, in your view, contain the most striking examples of effective descriptive language. For each of your examples, point out and explain the purpose behind the description and the specific techniques the author uses to achieve that purpose. Which different senses does the author appeal to? Prepare an oral reading of one of the passages; read expressively to capture the spirit of the description.

4. **Writing** *Survival Story* Like most survival stories, "A Marker on the Side of the Boat" contains a powerful external conflict. What is it? Are there other conflicts within the story as well? Write a survival story of your own in which one or more main characters must overcome an external conflict of some kind.

5. **Drama** *Setting the Stage* Use the details provided in the story to develop a sketch of a theatre or film stage for a production of "A Marker on the Side of the Boat." How will you repre-sent the various locales? What details will you emphasize? How will you light the stage to create an effective mood? Present your sketch to a small group, explaining your choices.

6. **Visual Communication** *Examine Photo* What information does this documentary photo convey? What assumptions does it prompt you to make as a viewer? Explain how the composition of the photo increases its impact.

My function as a writer is not story-telling
but truth-telling: to make things plain.
—Laura Riding Jackson

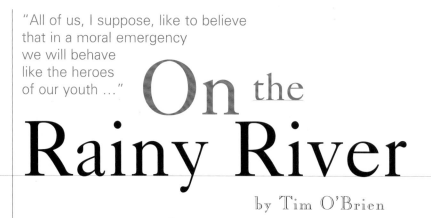

"All of us, I suppose, like to believe that in a moral emergency we will behave like the heroes of our youth ..."

On the Rainy River

by Tim O'Brien

This is one story I've never told before. Not to anyone. Not to my parents, not to my brother or sister, not even to my wife. To go into it, I've always thought, would only cause embarrassment for all of us, a sudden need to be elsewhere, which is the natural response to a confession. Even now, I'll admit, the story makes me squirm. For more than twenty years I've had to live with it, feeling the shame, trying to push it away, and so by this act of remembrance, by putting the facts down on paper, I'm hoping to relieve at least some of the pressure on my dreams. Still, it's a hard story to tell. All of us, I suppose, like to believe that in a moral emergency we will behave like the heroes of our youth, bravely and forthrightly, without thought of personal loss or discredit. Certainly that was my conviction back in the summer of 1968. Tim O'Brien: a secret hero. The Lone Ranger. If the stakes ever became high enough—if the evil were evil enough, if the good were good enough—I would simply tap a secret reservoir of courage that had been accumulating inside me over the years. Courage, I seemed to think, comes to us in finite quantities, like an inheritance, and by being frugal and stashing it away and letting it earn interest, we steadily increase our moral capital in preparation for that day when the account must be drawn down. It was a comforting theory. It dispensed with all those bothersome little acts of daily courage; it offered hope and grace to the repetitive coward; it justified the past while amortizing the future.

In June of 1968, a month after graduating from Macalester College, I was drafted to fight a war I hated.[1] I was twenty-one years old. Young, yes, and politically naive, but even so the American war in Vietnam seemed to me wrong. Certain blood was being shed for uncertain reasons. I saw no unity of purpose, no consensus on matters of philosophy or history or law. The very facts were shrouded in uncertainty: Was it a civil war? A war of national liberation or simple aggression? Who started it, and when, and why? What really happened to the USS *Maddox* on that dark night in the Gulf of Tonkin? Was Ho Chi Minh a Communist stooge, or a nationalist savior, or both, or neither? What about the Geneva Accords? What about SEATO and the Cold War? What about dominoes? America was divided on these and a thousand other issues, and the debate had spilled out across the floor of the United States Senate and into the streets, and smart men in pinstripes could not agree on even the most fundamental matters of public policy. The only certainty that summer was moral confusion. It was my view then, and still is, that you don't make war without knowing why. Knowledge, of course, is always imperfect, but it seemed to me that when a nation goes to war it must have reasonable confidence in the justice and imperative of its cause. You can't fix your mistakes. Once people are dead, you can't make them undead.

In any case those were my convictions, and back in college I had taken a modest stand against the war. Nothing radical, no hothead stuff, just ringing a few doorbells for Gene McCarthy, composing a few tedious, uninspired editorials for the campus newspaper. Oddly, though, it was almost entirely an intellectual activity. I brought some energy to it, of course, but it was the energy that accompanies almost any abstract endeavor; I felt no personal danger; I felt no sense of an impending crisis in my life. Stupidly, with a kind of smug removal that I can't begin to fathom, I assumed that the problems of killing and dying did not fall within my special province.

The draft notice arrived on June 17, 1968. It was a humid afternoon, I remember, cloudy and very quiet, and I'd just come in from a round of golf. My mother and father were having lunch out in the kitchen. I remember opening up the letter, scanning the first few lines, feeling the blood go thick behind my eyes. I remember a sound in my head. It wasn't thinking, it was just a silent howl. A million things all at

---

[1] **war I hated:** the Vietnam War, 1961–75; it began as a civil war between North and South Vietnam in the mid-1950s. By 1961, the Americans were actively involved in the war on the side of the South Vietnamese.

once—I was too *good* for this war. Too smart, too compassionate, too everything. It couldn't happen. I was above it. I had the world dicked—Phi Beta Kappa and summa cum laude and president of the student body and a full-ride scholarship for grad studies at Harvard. A mistake, maybe—a foul-up in the paperwork. I was no soldier. I hated Boy Scouts. I hated camping out. I hated dirt and tents and mosquitoes. The sight of blood made me queasy, and I couldn't tolerate authority, and I didn't know a rifle from a slingshot. I was a *liberal*, for Christ sake: If they needed fresh bodies, why not draft some back-to-the stone-age hawk? Or some dumb jingo in his hard hat and Bomb Hanoi button? Or one of LBJ's pretty daughters? Or Westmoreland's whole family—nephews and nieces and baby grandson? There should be a law, I thought. If you support a war, if you think it's worth the price, that's fine, but you have to put your own life on the line. You have to head for the front and hook up with an infantry unit and help spill the blood. And you have to bring along your wife, or your kids, or your lover. A *law*, I thought.

I remember the rage in my stomach. Later it burned down to a smoldering self-pity, then to numbness. At dinner that night my father asked what my plans were.

"Nothing," I said. "Wait."

I spent the summer of 1968 working in an Armour meatpacking plant in my hometown of Worthington, Minnesota. The plant specialized in pork products, and for eight hours a day I stood on a quarter-mile assembly line—more properly, a disassembly line—removing blood clots from the necks of dead pigs. My job title, I believe, was Declotter. After slaughter, the hogs were decapitated, split down the length of the belly, pried open, eviscerated, and strung up by the hind hocks on a high conveyer belt. Then gravity took over. By the time a carcass reached my spot on the line, the fluids had mostly drained out, everything except for thick clots of blood in the neck and upper chest cavity. To remove the stuff, I used a kind of water gun. The machine was heavy, maybe eighty pounds, and was suspended from the ceiling by a heavy rubber cord. There was some bounce to it, an elastic up-and-down give, and the trick was to maneuver the gun with your whole body, not lifting with the arms, just letting the rubber cord do the work for you. At one end was a trigger; at the muzzle end was a small nozzle and a steel roller brush. As a carcass passed by, you'd lean forward and swing the gun up against the clots and squeeze the trigger, all in one motion, and the brush would whirl and water would come shooting out and you'd hear a quick splattering sound as the clots dissolved into a fine red mist. It was not pleasant work. Goggles were a necessity, and a rubber apron, but even so it was like standing for eight hours a day under a lukewarm blood-shower. At night I'd go home smelling of pig. I couldn't wash it out. Even after a hot bath, scrubbing hard, the stink was always there—like old bacon, or sausage, a dense greasy pig-stink that soaked deep into my skin and hair. Among other things, I remember, it was tough getting dates that summer. I felt isolated; I spent a lot of time alone. And there was also that draft notice tucked away in my wallet.

In the evenings I'd sometimes borrow my father's car and drive aimlessly around town, feeling sorry for myself, thinking about the war and the pig factory and how my life seemed to be collapsing toward slaughter. I felt paralyzed. All around me the options seemed to be narrowing, as if I were hurtling down a huge black funnel, the whole world squeezing in tight. There was no happy way out. The government had ended most graduate school deferments; the waiting lists for the National Guard and Reserves were impossibly long; my health was solid; I didn't qualify for CO status[2]—no religious grounds, no history as a pacifist. Moreover, I could not claim to be opposed to war as a matter of general principle. There were occasions, I believed, when a nation was justified in using military force to achieve its ends, to stop a Hitler or some comparable evil, and I told myself that in such circumstances I would've willingly marched off to the battle. The problem, though, was that a draft board did not let you choose your war.

Beyond all this, or at the very center, was the raw fact of terror. I did not want to die. Not ever. But certainly not then, not there, not in a wrong war. Driving up Main Street, past the courthouse and the Ben Franklin store, I sometimes felt the fear spreading inside me like weeds. I imagined myself dead. I imagined myself doing things I could not do—charging an enemy position, taking aim at another human being.

At some point in mid-July I began thinking seriously about Canada. The border lay a few hundred miles north, an eight-hour drive. Both my conscience and my instincts were telling me to make a break for it, just take off and run like hell and never stop. In the beginning the idea seemed purely abstract, the word Canada printing itself out in my head; but after a time I could see particular shapes and images, the sorry details of my own future—a hotel room in Winnipeg, a battered old suitcase, my father's eyes as I tried to explain myself over the telephone.

---

[2] **CO status:** conscientious objector status. A conscientious objector resisted the war for reasons of religious or moral principle and could avoid military service.

I could almost hear his voice, and my mother's. Run, I'd think. Then I'd think, Impossible. Then a second later I'd think, *Run*.

It was a kind of schizophrenia. A moral split. I couldn't make up my mind. I feared the war, yes, but I also feared exile. I was afraid of walking away from my own life, my friends and my family, my whole history, everything that mattered to me. I feared losing the respect of my parents. I feared the law. I feared ridicule and censure. My hometown was a conservative little spot on the prairie, a place where tradition counted, and it was easy to imagine people sitting around a table down at the old Gobbler Café on Main Street, coffee cups poised, the conversation slowly zeroing in on the young O'Brien kid, how the damned sissy had taken off for Canada. At night, when I couldn't sleep, I'd sometimes carry on fierce arguments with those people. I'd be screaming at them, telling them how much I detested their blind, thoughtless, automatic acquiescence to it all, their simple-minded patriotism, their prideful ignorance, their love-it-or-leave-it platitudes, how they were sending me off to fight a war they didn't understand and didn't want to understand. I held them responsible. By God, yes, I *did*. All of them—I held them personally and individually responsible—the polyestered Kiwanis boys, the merchants and farmers, the pious churchgoers, the chatty housewives, the PTA and the Lions club and the Veterans of Foreign Wars and the fine upstanding gentry out at the country club. They didn't know Bao Dai[3] from the man in the moon. They didn't know history. They didn't know the first thing about Diem's tyranny, or the nature of Vietnamese nationalism, or the long colonialism of the French—this was all too damned complicated, it required some reading—but no matter, it was a war to stop the Communists, plain and simple, which was how they liked things, and you were a treasonous coward if you had second thoughts about killing or dying for plain and simple reasons.

I was bitter, sure. But it was so much more than that. The emotions went from outrage to terror to bewilderment to guilt to sorrow and then back again to outrage. I felt a sickness inside me. Real disease.

Most of this I've told before, or at least hinted at, but what I have never told is the full truth. How I cracked. How at work one morning, standing on the pig line, I felt something break open in my chest. I don't know what it was. I'll never know. But it was real, I know that much, it was a physical rupture—a cracking-leaking-popping feeling.

---

[3]**Bao Dai:** the last emperor of Vietnam. He abdicated his throne in 1945, but returned to power from 1949–55.

I remember dropping my water gun. Quickly, almost without thought, I took off my apron and walked out of the plant and drove home. It was midmorning, I remember, and the house was empty. Down in my chest there was still that leaking sensation, something very warm and precious spilling out, and I was covered with blood and hog-stink, and for a long while I just concentrated on holding myself together. I remember taking a hot shower. I remember packing a suitcase and carrying it out to the kitchen, standing very still for a few minutes, looking carefully at the familiar objects all around me. The old chrome toaster, the telephone, the pink and white Formica on the kitchen counters. The room was full of bright sunshine. Everything sparkled. My house, I thought. My life. I'm not sure how long I stood there, but later I scribbled out a short note to my parents.

What it said, exactly, I don't recall now. Something vague. Taking off, will call, love Tim.

I drove north.

It's a blur now, as it was then, and all I remember is a sense of high velocity and the feel of the steering wheel in my hands. I was riding on adrenaline. A giddy feeling, in a way, except there was the dreamy edge of impossibility to it—like running a dead-end maze—no way out—it couldn't come to a happy conclusion and yet I was doing it anyway because it was all I could think of to do. It was pure flight, fast and mindless. I had no plan. Just hit the border at high speed and crash through and keep on running. Near dusk I passed through Bemidji, then turned northeast toward International Falls. I spent the night in the car behind a closed-down gas station a half mile from the border. In the morning, after gassing up, I headed straight west along the Rainy River, which separates Minnesota from Canada, and which for me separated one life from another. The land was mostly wilderness. Here and there I passed a motel or bait shop, but otherwise the country unfolded in great sweeps of pine and birch and sumac. Though it was still August, the air already had the smell of October, football season, piles of yellow-red leaves, everything crisp and clean. I remember a huge blue sky. Off to my right was the Rainy River, wide as a lake in places, and beyond the Rainy River was Canada.

For a while I just drove, not aiming at anything, then in the late morning I began looking for a place to lie low for a day or two. I was exhausted, and scared sick, and around noon I pulled into an old fishing resort called the Tip Top Lodge. Actually it was not a lodge at all, just eight or nine tiny yellow cabins clustered on a peninsula that jutted northward into the Rainy River. The place was in sorry shape. There was a dangerous wooden dock, an old minnow tank, a flimsy tar paper boathouse along the shore. The main building, which stood in a cluster of pines on high ground, seemed to lean heavily to one side, like a cripple, the roof sagging toward Canada. Briefly, I thought about turning around, just giving up, but then I got out of the car and walked up to the front porch.

The man who opened the door that day is the hero of my life. How do I say this without sounding sappy? Blurt it out—the man saved me. He offered exactly what I needed, without questions, without any words at all. He took me in. He was there at the critical time—a silent, watchful presence. Six days later, when it ended, I was unable to find a proper way to thank him, and I never have, and so, if nothing else, this story represents a small gesture of gratitude twenty years overdue.

Even after two decades I can close my eyes and return to that porch at the Tip Top Lodge. I can see the old guy staring at me. Elroy Berdahl: eighty-one years old, skinny and shrunken and mostly bald. He wore a flannel shirt and brown work pants. In one hand, I remember, he carried a green apple, a small paring knife in the other. His eyes had the bluish gray color of a razor blade, the same polished shine, and as he peered up at me I felt a strange sharpness, almost painful, a cutting sensation, as if his gaze were somehow slicing me open. In part, no doubt, it was my own sense of guilt, but even so I'm absolutely certain that the old man took one look and went right to the heart of things—a kid in trouble. When I asked for a room, Elroy made a little clicking sound with his tongue. He nodded, led me out to one of the cabins, and dropped a key in my hand. I remember smiling at him. I also remember wishing I hadn't. The old man shook his head as if to tell me it wasn't worth the bother.

"Dinner at five-thirty," he said. "You eat fish?"

"Anything," I said.

Elroy grunted and said, "I'll bet."

We spent six days together at the Tip Top Lodge. Just the two of us. Tourist season was over, and there were no boats on the river, and the wilderness seemed to withdraw into a great permanent stillness. Over those six days Elroy Berdahl and I took most of our meals together. In the mornings we sometimes went out on long hikes into the woods, and at night we played Scrabble or listened to records or sat reading in front of his big stone fireplace. At times I felt the awkwardness of an intruder, but Elroy accepted me into his quiet routine without fuss or ceremony. He took my presence for granted, the same way he might've sheltered a stray cat—no wasted sighs or pity—and there was never any talk about it. Just the opposite. What I remember more than anything is the man's willful, almost ferocious silence. In all that time together, all those hours, he never asked the obvious questions: Why was I there? Why alone? Why so preoccupied? If Elroy was curious about any of this, he was careful never to put it into words.

My hunch, though, is that he already knew. At least the basics. After all, it was 1968, and guys were burning draft cards, and Canada was just a boat ride away. Elroy Berdahl was no hick. His bedroom, I remember, was cluttered with books and newspapers. He killed me at the Scrabble board, barely concentrating, and on those occasions when speech was necessary he had a way of compressing large thoughts into small, cryptic packets of language. One evening, just at sunset, he pointed up at an owl circling over the violet-lighted forest to the west.

"Hey, O'Brien," he said. "There's Jesus."

The man was sharp—he didn't miss much. Those razor eyes. Now and then he'd catch me staring out at the river, at the far shore, and I could almost hear the tumblers clicking in his head. Maybe I'm wrong, but I doubt it.

One thing for certain, he knew I was in desperate trouble. And he knew I couldn't talk about it. The wrong word—or even the right word—and I would've disappeared. I was wired and jittery. My skin felt too tight. After supper one evening I vomited and went back to my cabin and lay down for a few moments and then vomited again; another time, in the middle of the afternoon, I began sweating and couldn't shut it off. I went through whole days feeling dizzy with sorrow. I couldn't sleep; I couldn't lie still. At night I'd toss around in bed, half awake, half dreaming, imagining how I'd sneak down to the beach and quietly push one of the old man's boats out into the river and start paddling my way toward Canada. There were times when I thought I'd gone off the psychic edge. I couldn't tell up from down, I was just falling, and late in the night I'd lie there watching weird pictures spin through my head. Getting chased by the Border Patrol—helicopters and searchlights and barking dogs—I'd be crashing through the woods, I'd be down on my hands and knees—people shouting out my name—the law closing in on all sides—my hometown draft board and the FBI and the Royal Canadian Mounted Police. It all seemed crazy and impossible. Twenty-one years old, an ordinary kid with all the ordinary dreams and ambitions, and all I wanted was to live the life I was born to—a mainstream life—I loved baseball and hamburgers and cherry Cokes—and now I was off on the margins of exile, leaving my country forever, and it seemed so impossible and terrible and sad.

I'm not sure how I made it through those six days. Most of it I can't remember. On two or three afternoons, to pass some time, I helped

Elroy get the place ready for winter, sweeping down the cabins and hauling in the boats, little chores that kept my body moving. The days were cool and bright. The nights were very dark. One morning the old man showed me how to split and stack firewood, and for several hours we just worked in silence out behind his house. At one point, I remember, Elroy put down his maul and looked at me for a long time, his lips drawn as if framing a difficult question, but then he shook his head and went back to work. The man's self-control was amazing. He never pried. He never put me in a position that required lies or denials. To an extent, I suppose, his reticence was typical of that part of Minnesota, where privacy still held value, and even if I'd been walking around with some horrible deformity—four arms and three heads—I'm sure the old man would've talked about everything except those extra arms and heads. Simple politeness was part of it. But even more than that, I think, the man understood that words were insufficient. The problem had gone beyond discussion. During that long summer I'd been over and over the various arguments, all the pros and cons, and it was no longer a question that could be decided by an act of pure reason. Intellect had come up against emotion. My conscience told me to run, but some irrational and powerful force was resisting, like a weight pushing me toward the war. What it came down to, stupidly, was a sense of shame. Hot, stupid shame. I did not want people to think badly of me. Not my parents, not my brother and sister, not even the folks down at the Gobbler Café. I was ashamed to be there at the Tip Top Lodge. I was ashamed of my conscience, ashamed to be doing the right thing.

Some of this Elroy must've understood. Not the details, of course, but the plain fact of crisis.

Although the old man never confronted me about it, there was one occasion when he came close to forcing the whole thing out into the open. It was early evening, and we'd just finished supper, and over coffee and dessert I asked him about my bill, how much I owed so far. For a long while the old man squinted down at the tablecloth.

"Well, the basic rate," he said, "is fifty bucks a night. Not counting meals. This makes four nights, right?"

I nodded. I had three hundred and twelve dollars in my wallet.

Elroy kept his eyes on the tablecloth. "Now that's an on-season price. To be fair, I suppose we should knock it down a peg or two." He leaned back in his chair. "What's a reasonable number, you figure?"

"I don't know," I said. "Forty?"

"Forty's good. Forty a night. Then we tack on food—say another hundred? Two hundred sixty total?"

"I guess."

He raised his eyebrows. "Too much?"

"No, that's fair. It's fine. Tomorrow, though … I think I'd better take off tomorrow."

Elroy shrugged and began clearing the table. For a time he fussed with the dishes, whistling to himself as if the subject had been settled. After a second he slapped his hands together.

"You know what we forgot?" he said. "We forgot wages. Those odd jobs you done. What we have to do, we have to figure out what your time's worth. Your last job—how much did you pull in an hour?"

"Not enough," I said.

"A bad one?"

"Yes. Pretty bad."

Slowly then, without intending any long sermon, I told him about my days at the pig plant. It began as a straight recitation of the facts, but before I could stop myself I was talking about the blood clots and the water gun and how the smell had soaked into my skin and how I couldn't wash it away. I went on for a long time. I told him about wild hogs squealing in my dreams, the sounds of butchery, slaughterhouse sounds, and how I'd sometimes wake up with that greasy pig-stink in my throat.

When I was finished, Elroy nodded at me.

"Well, to be honest," he said, "when you first showed up here, I wondered about all that. The aroma, I mean. Smelled like you was awful damned fond of pork chops." The old man almost smiled. He made a snuffling sound, then sat down with a pencil and a piece of paper. "So what'd this crud job pay? Ten bucks an hour? Fifteen?"

"Less."

Elroy shook his head. "Let's make it fifteen. You put in twenty-five hours here, easy. That's three hundred seventy-five bucks total wages. We subtract the two hundred sixty for food and lodging, I still owe you a hundred and fifteen."

He took four fifties out of his shirt pocket and laid them on the table.

"Call it even," he said.

"No."

"Pick it up. Get yourself a haircut."

The money lay on the table for the rest of the evening. It was still there when I went back to my cabin. In the morning, though, I found an envelope tacked to my door. Inside were the four fifties and a two-word note that said EMERGENCY FUND.

The man knew.

Looking back after twenty years, I sometimes wonder if the events of that summer didn't happen in some other dimension, a place where your life exists before you've lived it, and where it goes afterward. None of it ever seemed real. During my time at the Tip Top Lodge I had the feeling that I'd slipped out of my own skin, hovering a few feet away while some poor yo-yo with my name and face tried to make his way toward a future he didn't understand and didn't want. Even now I can see myself as I was then. It's like watching an old home movie: I'm young and tan and fit. I've got hair—lots of it. I don't smoke or drink. I'm wearing faded blue jeans and a white polo shirt. I can see myself sitting on Elroy Berdahl's dock near dusk one evening, the sky a bright shimmering pink, and I'm finishing up a letter to my parents that tells what I'm about to do and why I'm doing it and how sorry I am that I'd never found the courage to talk to them about it. I ask them not to be angry. I try to explain some of my feelings, but there aren't enough words, and so I just say that it's a thing that has to be done. At the end of the letter I talk about the vacations we used to take up in this north country, at a place called Whitefish Lake, and how the scenery here reminds me of those good times. I tell them I'm fine. I tell them I'll write again from Winnipeg or Montreal or wherever I end up.

On my last full day, the sixth day, the old man took me out fishing on the Rainy River. The afternoon was sunny and cold. A stiff breeze came in from the north, and I remember how the little fourteen-foot boat made sharp rocking motions as we pushed off from the dock. The current was fast. All around us, I remember, there was a vastness to the world, an unpeopled rawness, just the trees and the sky and the water reaching out toward nowhere. The air had the brittle scent of October.

For ten or fifteen minutes Elroy held a course upstream, the river choppy and silver-gray, then he turned straight north and put the engine on full throttle. I felt the bow lift beneath me. I remember the wind in my ears, the sound of the old outboard Evinrude. For a time I didn't pay attention to anything, just feeling the cold spray against my face, but then it occurred to me that at some point we must've passed into Canadian waters, across that dotted line between two different worlds, and I remember a sudden tightness in my chest as I looked up and watched the far shore come at me. This wasn't a daydream. It was tangible and real. As we came in toward land, Elroy cut the engine, letting the boat fishtail lightly about twenty yards off shore. The old man didn't look at me or speak. Bending down, he opened up his tackle box and busied himself with a bobber and a piece of wire leader, humming to himself, his eyes down.

It struck me then that he must've planned it. I'll never be certain, of course, but I think he meant to bring me up against the realities, to guide me across the river and to take me to the edge and to stand a kind of vigil as I chose a life for myself.

I remember staring at the old man, then at my hands, then at Canada. The shoreline was dense with brush and timber. I could see tiny red berries on the bushes. I could see a squirrel up in one of the birch trees, a big crow looking at me from a boulder along the river. That close—twenty yards—and I could see the delicate latticework of the leaves, the texture of the soil, the browned needles beneath the pines, the configurations of geology and human history. Twenty yards. I could've done it. I could've jumped and started swimming for my life. Inside me, in my chest, I felt a terrible squeezing pressure. Even now, as I write this, I can still feel that tightness. And I want you to feel it—the wind coming off the river, the waves, the silence, the wooded frontier. You're at the bow of a boat on the Rainy River. You're twenty-one years old, you're scared, and there's a hard squeezing pressure in your chest.

What would you do?

Would you jump? Would you feel pity for yourself? Would you think about your family and your childhood and your dreams and all you're leaving behind? Would it hurt? Would it feel like dying? Would you cry, as I did?

I tried to swallow it back. I tried to smile, except I was crying.

Now, perhaps, you can understand why I've never told this story before. It's not just the embarrassment of tears. That's part of it, no doubt, but what embarrasses me much more, and always will, is the paralysis that took my heart. A moral freeze: I couldn't decide, I couldn't act, I couldn't comport myself with even a pretense of modest human dignity.

All I could do was cry. Quietly, not bawling, just the chest-chokes.

At the rear of the boat Elroy Berdahl pretended not to notice. He held a fishing rod in his hands, his head bowed to hide his eyes. He kept humming a soft, monotonous little tune. Everywhere, it seemed, in the trees and water and sky, a great worldwide sadness came pressing down on me, a crushing sorrow, sorrow like I had never known it before. And what was so sad, I realized, was that Canada had become a pitiful fantasy. Silly and hopeless. It was no longer a possibility. Right

> Fiction reveals truth that reality obscures.
>
> Jessamyn West

then, with the shore so close, I understood that I would not do what I should do. I would not swim away from my hometown and my country and my life. I would not be brave. That old image of myself as a hero, as a man of conscience and courage, all that was just a threadbare pipe dream. Bobbing there on the Rainy River, looking back at the Minnesota shore, I felt a sudden swell of helplessness come over me, a drowning sensation, as if I had toppled overboard and was being swept away by the silver waves. Chunks of my own history flashed by. I saw a seven-year-old boy in a white cowboy hat and a Lone Ranger mask and a pair of holstered six-shooters; I saw a twelve-year-old Little League shortstop pivoting to turn a double play; I saw a sixteen-year-old kid decked out for his first prom, looking spiffy in a white tux and a black bow tie, his hair cut short and flat, his shoes freshly polished. My whole life seemed to spill out into the river, swirling away from me, everything I had ever been or ever wanted to be. I couldn't get my breath; I couldn't stay afloat; I couldn't tell which way to swim. A hallucination, I suppose, but it was as real as anything I would ever feel. I saw my parents calling to me from the far shoreline. I saw my brother and sister, all the townsfolk, the mayor and the entire Chamber of Commerce and all my old teachers and girlfriends and high school buddies. Like some weird sporting event: everybody screaming from the sidelines, rooting me on—a loud stadium roar. Hotdogs and popcorn—stadium smells, stadium heat. A squad of cheerleaders did cartwheels along the banks of the Rainy River; they had megaphones and pompoms and smooth brown thighs. The crowd swayed left and right. A marching band played fight songs. All my aunts and uncles were there, and Abraham Lincoln, and Saint George, and a nine-year-old girl named Linda who had died of a brain tumor back in fifth grade, and several members of the United States Senate, and a blind poet scribbling notes, and LBJ, and Huck Finn, and Abbie Hoffman, and all the dead soldiers back from the grave, and the many thousands who were later to die—villagers with terrible burns, little kids without arms or legs—yes, and the Joint Chiefs of Staff were there, and a couple of popes, and a first lieutenant named Jimmy Cross, and the last surviving veteran of the American Civil War, and Jane Fonda dressed up as Barbarella, and an old man sprawled beside a pigpen, and my grandfather, and Gary Cooper, and a kind-faced woman carrying an umbrella and a copy of Plato's *Republic*, and a million ferocious citizens waving flags of all shapes and colors— people in hard hats, people in headbands—they were all whooping and chanting and urging me toward one shore or the other. I saw faces from my distant past and distant future. My wife was there. My unborn daughter waved at me, and my two sons hopped up and down, and a drill sergeant named Blyton sneered and shot up a finger and shook his head. There was a choir in bright purple robes. There was a cabbie from the Bronx. There was a slim young man I would one day kill with a hand grenade along a red clay trail outside the village of My Khe.

The little aluminum boat rocked softly beneath me. There was the wind and the sky.

I tried to will myself overboard.

I gripped the edge of the boat and leaned forward and thought, *Now.*

I did try. It just wasn't possible.

All those eyes on me—the town, the whole universe—and I couldn't risk the embarrassment. It was as if there were an audience to my life, that swirl of faces along the river, and in my head I could hear people screaming at me. Traitor! they yelled. Turncoat! Coward! I felt myself blush. I couldn't tolerate it. I couldn't endure the mockery, or the disgrace, or the patriotic ridicule. Even in my imagination, the shore just twenty yards away, I couldn't make myself be brave. It had nothing to do with morality. Embarrassment, that's all it was.

And right then I submitted.

I would go to the war—I would kill and maybe die—because I was embarrassed not to.

That was the sad thing. And so I sat in the bow of the boat and cried.

It was loud now. Loud, hard crying.

Elroy Berdahl remained quiet. He kept fishing. He worked his line with the tips of his fingers, patiently, squinting out at his red and white bobber on the Rainy River. His eyes were flat and impassive. He didn't speak. He was simply there, like the river and the late-summer sun. And yet by his presence, his mute watchfulness, he made it real. He was the true audience. He was a witness, like God, or like the gods, who look on in absolute silence as we live our lives, as we make our choices or fail to make them.

"Ain't biting," he said.

Then after a time the old man pulled in his line and turned the boat back toward Minnesota.

I don't remember saying goodbye. That last night we had dinner together, and I went to bed early, and in the morning Elroy fixed breakfast for me. When I told him I'd be leaving, the old man nodded as if he already knew. He looked down at the table and smiled.

At some point later in the morning it's possible that we shook hands—I just don't remember—but I do know that by the time I'd finished packing the old man had disappeared. Around noon, when I took my suitcase out to the car, I noticed that his old black pickup truck was no longer parked in front of the house. I went inside and waited for a while, but I felt a bone certainty that he wouldn't be back. In a way, I thought, it was appropriate. I washed up the breakfast dishes, left his two hundred dollars on the kitchen counter, got into the car, and drove south toward home.

The day was cloudy. I passed through towns with familiar names, through the pine forests and down to the prairie, and then to Vietnam, where I was a soldier, and then home again. I survived, but it's not a happy ending. I was a coward. I went to the war.

Tim O'Brien was born in Minnesota, U.S., in 1946. He graduated in 1968, after which he was drafted and sent to Vietnam. His division became involved in the My Lai massacre in 1968, which he wrote about later. After Vietnam, O'Brien attended Harvard, eventually leaving to become a newspaper reporter with the *Washington Post*. He soon gave up reporting to write fiction full time after his first book, *If I Die in a Combat Zone, Box Me Up and Send Me Home*. His other novels include *Northern Lights, Going After Cacciato, The Nuclear Age, The Things They Carried,* and *In the Lake of the Woods*.

I. *Response*

a. In your own words, summarize the reasons the narrator gives for his opposition to the Vietnam War.

b. The narrator's job at the Armour Meat Factory in some ways anticipates the experience of fighting in Vietnam. How? Do you think the author was right to include the graphic descriptions of the slaughterhouse? Explain.

c. In your opinion, does the reader need to have a personal knowledge of the issues regarding the Vietnam War to appreciate this story? Why or why not?

d. Reread the opening paragraph of the story. Now that you have read the whole account, why do you think the narrator waited so long to tell his story?

e. In a group, identify and discuss the emotional changes the narrator experiences as he moves toward his final decision. In your opinion, should he have accepted his draft notice, or should he have sought sanctuary in Canada as a draft-dodger?

2. ***Research and Inquiry*** Using the Internet and other resources, prepare a presentation for the class on American draft-dodgers and the Vietnam War. Try to find out how many young men dodged the draft at that time and what their reasons were. What was the reaction in the United States to these men at the time? What was the reaction after the war? Did the phenomenon of draft-dodging affect life in Canada in any way? Explain.

3. ***Literature Studies*** Fiction Versus Autobiography When you read "On the Rainy River," did you think of it as a story or an autobiographical account? Why? Actually, the story is a hybrid—it is based on O'Brien's experiences, but is not necessarily true in every detail. What are the benefits of this approach, from a writer's perspective? What is your own evaluation of this approach?

4. ***Film Study*** The Vietnam War has been the subject of a number of excellent films, for example, *Full Metal Jacket, Platoon, Apocalypse Now!*, and *Born on the Fourth of July*. View one of these films or another film about this war. Examine the protagonist's life and decisions. Write a brief essay to assess the difficulties he or she faces both physically and psychologically.

5. ***Making Connections*** Use a word web to explore the connotations and ideas that are evoked by the word *river*. Next, in an essay format, compare and contrast the symbolic value of the Honia River in "The Return" with that of the Rainy River in "On the Rainy River." Did your word web help to raise your awareness of these symbolic values? Explain.

    Alternatively, write an essay to compare and contrast the outlook on war presented by Bao Ninh in "A Marker on the Side of the Boat" with that presented by Tim O'Brien in "On the Rainy River." Include specific differences and similarities.

An unexpected sum of money propels
Mrs. Sommers into a most unusual day ...

A Pair of Silk Stockings

by Kate Chopin

Little Mrs. Sommers one day found herself the unexpected possessor of fifteen dollars. It seemed to her a very large amount of money, and the way in which it stuffed and bulged her worn old *porte-monnaie*[1] gave her a feeling of importance such as she had not enjoyed for years.

The question of investment was one that occupied her greatly. For a day or two she walked about apparently in a dreamy state, but really absorbed in speculation and calculation. She did not wish to act hastily, to do anything she might afterward regret. But it was during the still hours of the night when she lay awake revolving plans in her mind that she seemed to see her way clearly toward a proper and judicious use of the money.

A dollar or two should be added to the price usually paid for Janie's shoes, which would insure their lasting an appreciable time longer than they usually did. She would buy so and so many yards of percale[2] for new shirt waists[3] for the boys and Janie and Mag. She had intended to make the old ones do by skilful patching. Mag should have another gown. She had seen some beautiful patterns, veritable bargains in the shop windows. And still there would be left enough for new stockings—two pairs apiece—and what darning that would save for a while! She would get caps for the boys and sailor-hats for the girls. The vision of her little brood looking fresh and dainty and new for once in their lives excited her and made her restless and wakeful with anticipation.

[1] ***porte-monnaie:*** purse, wallet
[2] **percale:** a closely-woven cotton fabric
[3] **shirt waists:** a style of shirt popular in the late 1800s

The neighbors sometimes talked of certain "better days" that little Mrs. Sommers had known before she had ever thought of being Mrs. Sommers. She herself indulged in no such morbid retrospection. She had no time—no second of time to devote to the past. The needs of the present absorbed her every faculty. A vision of the future like some dim, gaunt monster sometimes appalled her, but luckily tomorrow never comes.

Mrs. Sommers was one who knew the value of bargains; who could stand for hours making her way inch by inch toward the desired object that was selling below cost. She could elbow her way if need be; she had learned to clutch a piece of goods and hold it and stick to it with persistence and determination till her turn came to be served, no matter when it came.

But that day she was a little faint and tired. She had swallowed a light luncheon—no! when she came to think of it, between getting the children fed and the place righted, and preparing herself for the shopping bout, she had actually forgotten to eat any luncheon at all!

She sat herself upon a revolving stool before a counter that was comparatively deserted, trying to gather strength and courage to charge through an eager multitude that was besieging breastworks[4] of shirting and figured lawn.[5] An all-gone limp feeling had come over her and she rested her hand aimlessly upon the counter. She wore no gloves. By degrees she grew aware that her hand had encountered something very soothing, very pleasant to touch. She looked down to see that her hand lay upon a pile of silk stockings. A placard near by announced that they had been reduced in price from two dollars and fifty cents to one dollar and ninety-eight cents; and a young girl who stood behind the counter asked her if she wished to examine their line of silk hosiery. She smiled, just as if she had been asked to inspect a tiara of diamonds with the ultimate view of purchasing it. But she went on feeling the soft, sheeny luxurious things—with both hands now, holding them up to see them glisten, and to feel them glide serpent-like through her fingers.

Two hectic blotches came suddenly into her pale cheeks. She looked up at the girl.

"Do you think there are any eights-and-a-half among these?"

There were any number of eights-and-a-half. In fact, there were more of that size than any other. Here was a light-blue pair;

[4]**breastworks:** chest-high counters (likened to the walls of a fort)
[5]**figured lawn:** cotton fabric woven with designs

there were some lavender, some all black and various shades of tan and gray. Mrs. Sommers selected a black pair and looked at them very long and closely. She pretended to be examining their texture, which the clerk assured her was excellent.

"A dollar and ninety-eight cents," she mused aloud. "Well, I'll take this pair." She handed the girl a five-dollar bill and waited for her change and for her parcel. What a very small parcel it was! It seemed lost in the depths of her shabby old shopping-bag.

Mrs. Sommers after that did not move in the direction of the bargain counter. She took the elevator, which carried her to an upper floor into the region of the ladies' waiting-rooms. Here, in a retired corner, she exchanged her cotton stockings for the new silk ones which she had just bought. She was not going through any acute mental process or reasoning with herself, nor was she striving to explain to her satisfaction the motive of her action. She was not thinking at all. She seemed for the time to be taking a rest from that laborious and fatiguing function and to have abandoned herself to some mechanical impulse that directed her actions and freed her of responsibility.

How good was the touch of the raw silk to her flesh! She felt like lying back in the cushioned chair and reveling for a while in the luxury of it. She did for a little while. Then she replaced her shoes, rolled the cotton stockings together and thrust them into her bag. After doing this she crossed straight over to the shoe department and took her seat to be fitted.

She was fastidious. The clerk could not make her out; he could not reconcile her shoes with her stockings, and she was not too easily pleased. She held back her skirts and turned her feet one way and her head another way as she glanced down at the polished, pointed-tipped boots. Her foot and ankle looked very pretty. She could not realize that they belonged to her and were a part of herself. She wanted an excellent and stylish fit, she told the young fellow who served her, and she did not mind the difference of a dollar or two more in the price so long as she got what she desired.

It was a long time since Mrs. Sommers had been fitted with gloves. On rare occasions when she had bought a pair they were always "bargains," so cheap that it would have been preposterous and unreasonable to have expected them to be fitted to the hand.

Now she rested her elbow on the cushion of the glove counter, and a pretty, pleasant young creature, delicate and deft of touch, drew a long-wristed "kid"[6] over Mrs. Sommers's hand. She smoothed it down over

---

[6]**kid:** kid gloves, made from the skin of a young goat

the wrist and buttoned it neatly, and both lost themselves for a second or two in admiring contemplation of the little symmetrical gloved hand. But there were other places where money might be spent.

There were books and magazines piled up in the window of a stall a few paces down the street. Mrs. Sommers bought two high-priced magazines such as she had been accustomed to read in the days when she had been accustomed to other pleasant things. She carried them without wrapping. As well as she could she lifted her skirts at the crossings. Her stockings and boots and well fitting gloves had worked marvels in her bearing—had given her a feeling of assurance, a sense of belonging to the well-dressed multitude.

She was very hungry. Another time she would have stilled the cravings for food until reaching her own home, where she would have brewed herself a cup of tea and taken a snack of anything that was available. But the impulse that was guiding her would not suffer her to entertain any such thought.

There was a restaurant at the corner. She had never entered its doors; from the outside she had sometimes caught glimpses of spotless damask[7] and shining crystal, and soft-stepping waiters serving people of fashion.

When she entered her appearance created no surprise, no consternation, as she had half feared it might. She seated herself at a small table alone, and an attentive waiter at once approached to take her order. She did not want a profusion; she craved a nice and tasty bite—a half dozen blue-points,[8] a plump chop with cress, a something sweet —a crème-frappée,[9] for instance; a glass of Rhine wine, and after all a small cup of black coffee.

While waiting to be served she removed her gloves very leisurely and laid them beside her. Then she picked up a magazine and glanced through it, cutting the pages[10] with a blunt edge of her knife. It was all very agreeable. The damask was even more spotless than it had seemed through the window, and the crystal more sparkling. There were quiet ladies and gentlemen, who did not notice her, lunching at the small tables like her own. A soft, pleasing strain of music could be heard, and a gentle breeze was blowing through the window. She tasted a bite, and she read a word or two, and she sipped the amber wine and wiggled her toes in the silk stockings. The price of it made no

---

[7]**damask:** fine table linen
[8]**blue-points:** a kind of oyster
[9]**crème-frappée:** a frozen dessert
[10]**cutting the pages:** At one time, the pages of some books and magazines were attached and had to be sliced apart along one or more sides.

difference. She counted the money out to the waiter and left an extra coin on his tray, whereupon he bowed before her as before a princess of royal blood.

There was still money in her purse, and her next temptation presented itself in the shape of a matinée poster.

It was a little later when she entered the theatre, the play had begun and the house seemed to her to be packed. But there were vacant seats here and there, and into one of them she was ushered, between brilliantly dressed women who had gone there to kill time and eat candy and display their gaudy attire. There were many others who were there solely for the play and acting. It is safe to say there was no one present who bore quite the attitude which Mrs. Sommers did to her surroundings. She gathered in the whole—stage and players and people in one wide impression, and absorbed it and enjoyed it. She laughed at the comedy and wept—she and the gaudy woman next to her wept over the tragedy. And they talked a little together over it. And the gaudy woman wiped her eyes and sniffled on a tiny square of filmy, perfumed lace and passed little Mrs. Sommers her box of candy.

The play was over, the music ceased, the crowd filed out. It was like a dream ended. People scattered in all directions. Mrs. Sommers went to the corner and waited for the cable car.

A man with keen eyes, who sat opposite to her, seemed to like the study of her small, pale face. It puzzled him to decipher what he saw there. In truth, he saw nothing—unless he were wizard enough to detect a poignant wish, a powerful longing that the cable car would never stop anywhere, but go on and on with her forever.

Kate Chopin was born in St. Louis, U.S., in 1850. Several of her stories were published in magazines such as *America*, the *St. Louis Post-Dispatch*, and *Vogue*. Her first novel, *At Fault*, was published privately, after which she submitted her novel *Young Dr. Gosse* to several publishers, but was unsuccessful. She went on to publish several other works, including her well-known novel, *The Awakening*, which received scathing reviews. She died in 1904. Although her work remained more or less forgotten for some time, *The Awakening* is now widely read, and regarded as an important feminist work.

1. *Response*

a. What details is the reader given about Mrs. Sommers' life before her shopping trip? Explain how these details are important to the story's meaning.

b. Mrs. Sommers "did not wish to act hastily, to do anything she might afterward regret." Find the point in the story where she abandons her careful planning. Based on what you know about Mrs. Sommers' character, and about people in general, do you find this shift convincing? Why or why not?

c. Reread the final paragraph of the story. What is the impact of closing the story in this manner?

d. This story was published in 1894. In your view, does it have any relevance for today's readers? Explain.

2. *Language Conventions* *Formal Tone* Select five specific examples that illustrate the formal diction and prose style Chopin uses in this story. Do you think the style is appropriate to Mrs. Sommers' situation and to the story's theme? Explain.

3. *Literature Studies* *Character Analysis* Write a character analysis of Mrs. Sommers in which you describe and explain how she changes in this story. Include specific references to details that illustrate the **dynamic** nature of her character. Do you think these changes are temporary or permanent?

A **dynamic character** is one who undergoes a significant and permanent change in personality or beliefs.

4. *Drama* *Improvisation* What will unfold when, wearing her new clothes, Mrs. Sommers returns home to her family but with all her money spent? In a group, improvise the scene. Before you make your presentation, have a group discussion in which you agree on the state of mind of each character.

5. *Making Connections* In "Transients in Arcadia" and "A Pair of Silk Stockings," the characters have a powerful desire for a moment of luxury and the appearance of upper-class distinction. What are the similarities and differences between Mrs. Sommers and Mamie Siviter? Imagine what the two women might say to each other if they met at the hosiery counter at Casey's store. With a partner, role-play the conversation.

Dressing Up for the Carnival

by Carol Shields

All over town people are putting on their costumes. Tamara has flung open her closet door; just to see her standing there is to feel a squeeze of the heart. She loves her clothes. She *knows* her clothes. Her favourite moment of the day is *this* moment, standing at the closet door, still a little dizzy from her long night of tumbled sleep, biting her lip, thinking hard, moving the busy hangers along the rod, about to make up her mind.

Yes! The yellow cotton skirt with the big patch pockets and the hand detail around the hem. How fortunate to own such a skirt. And the white blouse. What a blouse! Those sleeves, that neckline with its buttoned flap, the fullness in the yoke that reminds her of the Morris dances she and her boyfriend Bruce saw at the Exhibition last year.

Next she adds her new straw belt; perfect. A string of yellow beads. Earrings of course. Her bone sandals. And bare legs, why not?

She never checks the weather before she dresses; her clothes *are* the weather, as powerful in their sunniness as the strong, muzzy early morning light pouring into the narrow street by the bus stop, warming the combed crown of her hair and fuelling her with imagination. She taps a sandalled foot lightly on the pavement, waiting for the number 4 bus, no longer just Tamara, clerk-receptionist for the Youth Employment Bureau, but a woman in a yellow skirt. A passionate woman dressed in yellow. A Passionate, Vibrant Woman About To Begin Her Day. Her Life.

Roger, aged thirty, employed by the Gas Board, is coming out of a corner grocer's carrying a mango in his left hand. He went in to buy an apple and came out with *this*. At the cash register he refused

Business Man Wearing Mask by Curtis Parker.

a bag, preferring to carry this thing, this object, in his bare hand. The price was $1.29. He's a little surprised at how heavy it is, a tight seamless leather skin enclosing soft pulp, or so he imagines. He has never bought a mango before, never eaten one, doesn't know what a mango tastes like or how it's prepared. Cooked like a squash? Sliced and sugared like a peach? He has no intention of eating it, not now anyway, maybe never. Its weight reminds him of a first-class league ball, but larger, longer, smooth skinned, and ripely green. Mango, mango. An elliptical purse, juice-filled, curved for the palm of the human hand, his hand.

He is a man of medium height, burly, divorced, wearing an open-necked shirt, hurrying back to work after his coffee break. But at this moment he freezes and sees himself freshly: a man carrying a mango in his left hand. Already he's accustomed to it; in fact, it's starting to feel lighter and drier, like a set of castanets which has somehow attached itself to his left arm. Any minute now he'll break out into a cha-cha-cha right here in front of the Gas Board. The shrivelled fate he sometimes sees for himself can be postponed if only he puts his mind to it. Who would have thought it of him? Not his ex-wife Lucile, not his co-workers, not his boss, not even himself.

And the Borden sisters are back from their ski week in Happy Valley. They've been back for a month now, in fact, so why are they still wearing those little plastic ski passes on the zipper tabs of their jackets? A good question. I SKIED HAPPY MOUNTAIN these passes say. The Bordens wear them all over town, at the shopping centre, in the parking lot. It's spring, the leaves are unfolding on the hedges in front of the post office, but the Borden girls, Karen and Sue, still carry on their bodies, and in their faces too, the fresh wintry cold of the slopes, the thrill of powder snow and stinging sky. (The air up there chimes with echoes, a bromide of blue.) It would be an exaggeration to say the Borden sisters swagger; it would be going too far. They move like young ponies, quivery and thoughtful, with the memory of expended effort and banked curves. They speak to each other in voices that are loud and musical, and their skin, so clear, pink, bright, and healthy, traps the sunshine beneath its surface. With one hand, walking along, they stroke the feathering-out tops of hedges in front of the post office, and with the other they pull and tug on those little plasticized tags—I SKIED HAPPY MOUNTAIN. You might say it's a kind of compulsion, as though they can't help themselves.

And then there's Wanda from the bank who has been sent on the strangest of errands. It happened in this way: Mr. Wishcourt, the bank manager where Wanda works, has just bought a new baby carriage for his wife, or rather, for their new baby son, Samuel James. The baby carriage was an impulsive lunch-hour purchase, he explains to Wanda, looking shamefaced but exuberant: an English pram, high-wheeled, majestically hooded, tires like a Rolls Royce, a beauty, but the fool thing, even when folded up, refuses to fit in the back of his Volvo. Would she object? It would take perhaps three-quarters of an hour. It's a fine day. He'll draw her a plan on a sheet of paper, put an X where his house is. He knows how she loves walking, that she gets restless in the afternoon sometimes, sitting in her little airless cage. He would appreciate it so much. And so would his wife and little Sam. Would she mind? He's never before asked her to make coffee or do personal errands. It's against his policy, treating his employees like that. But just this once?

Wanda sets off awkwardly. She is, after all, an awkward woman, who was formerly an awkward girl with big girlish teeth and clumsy shoulders. The pram's swaying body seems to steer her at first, instead of *her* steering *it*. Such a chunky rolling oblong, black and British with its wambling,[1] bossy, outsized keel. "Excuse me," she says, and "Sorry." Without meaning to, she forces people over to the edge of the sidewalks, crowds them at the street corners, even rubs up against them with the big soft tires.

All she gets back are smiles. Or kindly little nods that say: "It's not your fault" or "How marvellous" or "What a picture!" After a bit she gets the hang of steering. This is a technical marvel she's pushing along, the way it takes the curbs, soundlessly, with scarcely any effort at all. Engineering at its most refined and comical. Her hands rest lightly on the wide white handlebar. It might be made of ivory or alabaster or something equally precious, it's so smooth and cool to the touch.

By the time Wanda reaches Pine Street she feels herself fully in charge. Beneath the leafy poplars, she and the carriage have become a single entity. Gliding, melding, a silvery hum of wheels and a faint, pleasing adhesive resistance as the tires roll along suburban asphalt. The weight of her fingertips is enough to keep it in motion, in control, and she takes the final corners with grace. Little Sam is going to love his new rolling home, so roomy and rhythmic, like a dark boat sailing forward in tune with his infant breathing and the bump-dee-bump of his baby heart.

She stops, leans over, and reaches inside. There's no one about; no one sees her, only the eyes inside her head that have rehearsed this small gesture in dreams. She straightens the blanket, pulling it smooth,

---

[1]**wambling:** wobbling, rolling

pats it into place. "Shhh," she murmurs, smiling. "There, there, now."

Mr. Gilman is smiling too. His daughter-in-law, who considers him a prehistoric bore, has invited him to dinner. This happens perhaps once a month; the telephone rings early in the morning. "We'd love to have you over tonight," she says. "Just family fare, I'm afraid, leftovers."

"I'd be delighted," he always says, even though the word *leftovers* gives him, every time she says it, a little ping of injury.

At age eighty he can be observed in his obverse infancy, metaphorically sucking and tonguing the missing tooth of his life. He knows what he looks like: the mirror tells all—eyes like water sacs, crimson arcs around the ears, a chin that betrays him, the way it mooches and wobbles while he thrashes around in his head for one of those rumpled anecdotes that seem only to madden his daughter-in-law. Better to keep still and chew. "Scrumptious," he always says, hoping to win her inhospitable heart, but knowing he can't.

Today he decides to buy her flowers. Why-oh-why has he never thought of this before! Daffodils are selling for $1.99 a half dozen. A bargain. It must be spring, he thinks, looking around. Why not buy two bunches, or three? Why not indeed? Or four?

They form a blaze of yellow in his arms, a sweet propitiating little fire. He knows he should take them home immediately and put them in water for tonight, but he's reluctant to remove the green paper wrapping which lends a certain legitimacy; these aren't flowers randomly snatched from the garden; these are florist's flowers, purchased as an offering, an oblation.[2]

There seems nothing to do but carry them about with him all day. He takes them along to the bank, the drugstore, to his appointment with the foot specialist, his afternoon card club at the Sunset Lodge. Never has he received more courteous attention, such quick service. The eyes of strangers appear friendlier than usual. "I am no worse off than the average person," he announces to himself. He loses, gracefully, at canasta, then gets a seat on the bus, a seat by the window. The pale flowers in his arms spell evanescence, gaiety. "Hello there," a number of people call out to him. He is clearly a man who is expected somewhere, anticipated. A charming gent, elegant and dapper, propounding serious questions, bearing gifts, flowers. A man in disguise.

Ralph Eliot, seventeen years old, six feet tall, killingly handsome, and the best halfback the school team has seen in years, has carelessly left his football helmet hanging on a hook on the back of his bedroom

---

[2]**oblation:** an offering or gift

door. An emergency of the first order; his ten-year-old sister Mandy is summoned to bring it to the playing field.

She runs all the way up Second Avenue; at the traffic light she strikes a pose, panting, then pounds furiously the whole length of Sargent Street, making it in four minutes flat. She carries the helmet by its tough plastic chin strap and as she runs along, it bangs against her bare leg. She feels her breath blazing into a spray of heroic pain, and as her foot rounds on the pavement a filament of recognition is touched. The exactitude of the gesture doubles and divides inside her head, and for the first time she comprehends *who* her brother is, that deep-voiced stranger whose bedroom is next to her own. Today, for a minute, she *is* her brother. *She* is Ralph Eliot, age seventeen, six feet tall, who later this afternoon will make a dazzling, lazy touchdown, bringing reward and honour to his name, and hers.

Susan Gourley, first-year arts student, has been assigned Beckett's *Waiting for Godot*.[3] She carries it under her arm so that the title is plainly visible. She is a girl with a look of lustreless inattention and a reputation for drowsiness, but she's always known this to be a false assessment. She's biding her time, waiting; today she strides along, *strides*, her book flashing under her arm. She is a young woman who is reading a great classic. Vistas of possibility unfold like money.

Molly Beale's briny old body has been propelled downtown by her cheerful new pacemaker, and there she bumps into Bert Lessing, the city councillor, whose navy blue beret, complete with military insignia, rides pertly over his left ear. They converse like lovers. They bristle with wit. They chitter like birds.

Jeanette Foster is sporting a smart chignon. Who does she think she *is*! Who *does* she think she is?

A young woman, recently arrived in town and rather lonely, carries her sandwiches to work in an old violin case. This is only temporary. Tomorrow she may use an ordinary paper bag or eat in the cafeteria.

We cannot live without our illusions, thinks X, an anonymous middle-aged citizen who, sometimes, in the privacy of his own bedroom, in the embrace of happiness, waltzes about in his wife's lace-trimmed nightgown. His wife is at bingo, not expected home for an hour. He lifts the blind an inch and sees the sun setting boldly behind his pear tree, its mingled coarseness and refinement giving an air of confusion. Everywhere he looks he observes cycles of consolation and enhancement, and now it seems as though the evening itself is about to alter its dimensions, becoming more (and also less) than what it really is. ▶

---

[3]**Beckett's *Waiting for Godot*:** famous absurdist drama, written in 1949

Carol Shields was born in Illinois, U.S., in 1935. She studied
at Hanover College, the University of Exeter in England,
and at the University of Ottawa, and moved to Canada
in the 1950s. She has worked as a professor, lecturing at
several Canadian universities, and is the author of a number
of novels and short story collections. Her writing has won a
Canada Council Major Award, the Canadian Author's Award,
two National Magazine Awards, a CBC Award, and the
Governor General's Award. Her books include
Small Ceremonies, Swann, The Box Garden, and *Larry's Party.*

1. *Response*

a. Make a list of the characters in the story, jotting down
what each is wearing or carrying, and what that tells you
about the character. Do you see a pattern or progression
from the first characters to those in the closing paragraphs?
Again, jot down your ideas in your notebook.

b. Comment on the title of the story. What is "the carnival"?

c. What are some of the ideas this story seems to be
expressing? What do you think Carol Shields' purpose was in
writing it?

d. Did you like this story? Explain your answer. Have you read
any other stories with a similar style?

2. *Literature Studies* Short Story Elements

Which short story
elements does "Dressing Up for the Carnival" contain? In
your view, what is the predominant element? Explore these
questions in a small group. One group member should be
prepared to present your conclusions to the class. Include
specific references to the story in your presentation.

3. *Writing* Storytelling

Create another episode for "Dressing
Up for the Carnival," exploring the perspective of another
character placed in this town. You might imitate Shields'
writing style and/or expand on her ideas or themes. After
your writing is complete, go back to the story and see where
your episode would best fit. Did you find it easy or difficult to
match your writing with that of Shields? Explain.

4. **Film Study** With a partner, develop a proposal for a film adaptation of this story. How would a filmmaker capture the atmosphere of the story and convey the ideas Shields presents? Your proposal should consider some or all of the following aspects of the film: atmosphere, setting, character (who you would cast), dialogue (whether you would add conversation), music/sound effects, and film technique (camera angles, shots, editing techniques). It should also include a storyboard for one scene of the film. Present your proposal and storyboard to the class, giving your reasons for the choices you made.

5. **Visual Communication** *Illustrating the Story* In a sentence or two, state your ideas about what the painting that accompanies this story might be saying. Next, compare and contrast *Business Man Wearing Mask* by Curtis Parker with "Dressing Up for the Carnival." Consider content, style, and tone in your analysis.

Theme Connections

- *"Transients in Arcadia,"* a story in which characters present a false front to others, Vol. I, p. 37
- *"A Pair of Silk Stockings,"* a story in which a character tries to create a new self, Vol. I, p. 86
- *"On the Value of Fantasies,"* a poem about the importance of dreaming of better lives, Vol. I, p. 184
- *"The Love Song of J. Alfred Prufrock,"* a poem about keeping up appearances, Vol. I, p. 240
- *"Introducing Cyrano,"* a play excerpt in which physical appearance plays an important role, Vol. II, p. 218

"She wanted out of this skin, out of this life and into another, one that fit her, not one that she had to fit."

The Spaces Between Stars

by Geeta Kothari

WATCHING THE FISH SQUIRM IN EVAN'S GLOVED HANDS, Maya was transfixed by the fish's suffering. It had stopped moving for a second, but now it was struggling, its tail flapping back and forth, as it twisted for freedom, unaware that the hook lodged deep in its gut wouldn't let go.

"It's dying," she said. "We should have pushed down the barbs like that woman in the store told us to."

Evan grunted and peered inside the fish's mouth.

"I know what I'm doing."

Maya knew he was determined to give her a genuine, all-American fishing trip, the kind he used to go on when he was a boy outdoors, and she was a girl indoors, watching TV. Long before Evan, there had been a boy on TV, a boy with long lanky hair that hung across one eye. He had flicked it back impatiently as he baited the hook, explaining to the camera that the "crick" was his favourite place. She remembered that word "crick" because some of the kids at school said it, kids who were unaware of her but whom she observed from a distance.

The small sunfish, a swath of green and gold, glistened in Evan's hand. The sun beat down on the top of Maya's head, searing her scalp. She felt dizzy and a wave of sadness passed over her as she stared at the helpless fish.

"It's dying."

Evan gently placed the sunfish in the water and cut the line. It swam off, seemingly recovered from its near-death experience.

To cook the fish he had caught, the boy on TV dug up some fresh clay, patted it into two flat rounds, stuck the fish between them and baked it in the flames of his campfire. In her dreams, Maya would camp by that "crick," fish and swim in it and sleep in a tent under the stars. How she would see the stars above her head while sleeping in a tent, she wasn't sure, but even in her fantasy life, she could not see herself sleeping without shelter.

Maya climbed back into the boat. Her line had been cut, and her mission had been achieved. She proved herself able to catch a fish, and now she wanted to go home. She handed Evan a turkey sandwich and looked over the side of the boat. Her fish, red at the gills, eyes bulging, floated towards them.

"Look," she said. "It died anyway."

Evan shrugged. "It was just a sunfish. They're everywhere."

Her guilt pressed against her temples, tightening like a vice around her head. Still she said nothing. She'd been the one who not only agreed but had been excited about going fishing. It had been one of the many activities forbidden to her during childhood. The expedition should have made her feel closer to Evan. Instead, Maya felt as if the parched brown hills surrounding the lake had sprung up between them. The inside of her skin itched, and she wanted to jump out of it, leave behind her body and the pervasive smell of dead fish.

She watched Evan eat his sandwich, oblivious to her inner turmoil as he basked in the sun. He was like that boy on TV. He was resourceful, knew how to do things that were beyond her realm of experience. He could pitch a tent, start a campfire, handle raw meat without feeling sick, open the hood of a car and see things. He could talk to strangers and get his way. Evan assumed he had the right number until told otherwise; he assumed cooperation and satisfaction, even when talking to the phone company about a bill. Making calls from one of her temporary jobs, Maya would begin her sentences with "I'm not sure ..." and end them breathless, gasping for air, as she struggled to find the right words. Eventually, passed from one person to the next, trying to make herself understood, she would give up and leave the task for the next day. What looked like procrastination was something she couldn't begin to explain.

She had wanted to be that boy on TV, but what such boys were seemed hereditary, increasingly out of reach and unattainable. Instead, she forced herself through college and one dismal semester of graduate school. And then she married Evan.

They got home late in the afternoon, just as the thunder started rolling in. Evan shut himself in his study while Maya napped. The heat, the death of the fish, had exhausted her leaving her empty and dry inside.

Later, she made dinner, though she had no appetite or enthusiasm for the aloo gobi[1] and dal.[2] Nothing smelled or tasted right; the potatoes and cauliflower were mushy and the dal was limp and tasteless. Her shoulders felt sore from the sun, and the smell of blood lingered on her fingers. She felt dirty, stained by the death of the sunfish. She rubbed her fingers with lemon juice until her cuticles burned, and still they smelled.

Evan padded into the kitchen, his blond hair sticking up as if he'd been sleeping and pulled a beer out of the refrigerator.

"Indian food. What's the occasion?" He leaned against the counter and stretched his legs across the narrow passage. Everything about him was long, lean and graceful. Next to him, she felt like a clumsy baby elephant—small, dark, and always in his shadow.

"None. Should there be?"

"You never make it, that's all."

"That's because I can't." Her voice got tighter and she felt a rush of anger, making her face hotter above the steaming pots.

But Evan would not be drawn into a fight. "Don't forget, my folks are coming next week. And they want an answer about the trip."

Maya's stomach dropped. She'd forgotten both the ski trip at Christmas and the Everetts' impending visit.

Fortunately, the Everetts would stay with friends, as they always did. Though they'd never said anything, Maya sensed that she didn't keep house up to their standards. The brass incense holder, the small footstool inlaid with ivory, the embroidered mirror-work cushions, and the orange and red batik wall hangings had been passed on to her by her aunt, Shyamma. They seemed to go well with the reupholstered couch and chair from Evan's parents, but she was sure they didn't find the same comfort in this mixed decor.

Maya checked the cumin-flavoured rice. When she looked up, she noticed that Evan was still in the room, watching her as she moved from stove to sink, counter to kitchen table. "Are you all right?" he asked.

"Fine." He was the psychologist, she thought. Let him figure it out.

"Really?" He came over and kissed the back of her neck while she fluffed the rice. The individual grains had lost their definition and clung together, exactly what the recipe warned against.

"Allergies," she said, shrugging him off. Her long dark hair was coming out of its elastic band, sticking to the back of her sweaty neck.

---

[1]**aloo gobi:** a vegetable curry, mainly of cauliflower and potatoes
[2]**dal:** a dish containing lentils

His lips against her skin reminded her of the fish, gasping for breath.

She couldn't tell him. She couldn't admit her failure of will, of heart, in the great American outdoors. It was simply beyond her, to find the words for this thing she couldn't understand.

After dinner, Shyamma called.

First, she complained about the weather.

"Yesterday, I forgot to drink even one glass of water. Can you imagine? I nearly fainted in the kitchen."

"You have to pay attention, auntie." Maya could not call her Shyamma, the way Evan did, not out loud, even though Shyamma had told her to. "The heat isn't your friend, just because you don't like the cold."

Three, four times a week, Shyamma would call with a muted crisis or a question that needed an immediate response. A response, not an answer, Maya finally understood, and she listened, for Shyamma was the only family she had.

"And how is that husband of yours?"

"Fine. He's nearly finished." Evan was working on his dissertation, and it gave Shyamma great pleasure to finally have a PhD in the family. Evan's success made up nicely for the brilliant failure of Maya's academic career.

Maya wondered what Shyamma would say about her aborted conversion into a fisherwoman and her complicity in the death of the sunfish. What was okay for an Everett might be unacceptable for a Sohni. Shyamma was still a vegetarian. She prayed to her blue-faced gods and goddesses,[3] and every day at sunset, burnt sweetgrass and sage on a small piece of charcoal, carrying it reverently from room to room in the small house Maya had grown up in.

Shyamma asked about the Everetts, their two daughters, and everyone else under the Everett sun.

"Such a nice family." She sighed.

"Because they invite you to their stupid Christmas party?" Maya chewed a hangnail, enjoying the sharp pain that ran through her finger.

"Yes. And they always send me cards—Halloween, Easter, Christmas."

Holidays Shyamma used to dismiss as "Christian" or "American," having nothing to do with them. Not even a Christmas tree, Maya thought, and now she eats cookies shaped like Santa Claus and sings

---

[3]**blue-faced gods and goddesses:** Hindu deities such as Vishnu and Shiva are sometimes depicted with blue faces and skin.

"Away in the Manger" without hesitation. After five years, she knew the words by heart, just like everyone else at the party.

"And so," Shyamma finally said, "How are you?"

"Fine. We went fishing today."

"That's nice, bacchi."[4] Maya listened to the pots and pan clattering in the background. She doubted her aunt had heard her. Their conversation was over.

Shyamma had raised Maya alone, after her parents were killed in a plane crash. Rather than send Maya back to live with her paternal grandparents, Shyamma insisted on keeping her in the States. She herself didn't want to go back to India and marry the demented distant cousin her father had found for her.

"Understand," Shyamma once said, "I had a fellowship, and I was finally free. And I was afraid if I sent you to your father's people, we'd never see you."

They had been lonely in Erie. They knew no other Indian families with children. Most of Shyamma's friends were single women who worked full-time. She seemed not to miss her family whom they saw on rare visits to Delhi. Now, though, her loneliness had caught up with her. Maya heard it in the phone calls, the unasked "When are you next coming up?" During those cold, dreary winters, when the wind blew hard off the lake and kept them inside, Shyamma would tell Maya what a great life they had, how easy it was to be American, how good this country had been to her. But for Maya, growing up in a strict vegetarian household in Erie during the sixties was not fun. Her aunt, Shyamma, banned Oreos because they were made with lard. At barbecues and school picnics, Maya hid her plate, heavy with potato salad, corn on the cob, coleslaw and an empty hot dog bun. Shyamma saw to it that Maya ate nutritionally sound meals, overlooking the conflict between this and Maya's sole desire: to be like everyone else and not like her aunt, who still lived in the culture she'd left over thirty years ago.

On their last trip to Erie, Maya and Evan had found Shyamma chilled and sick with the flu. She had hid it from them, she said, because she was afraid they wouldn't come up. The walk at Presque Isle, promised to Evan, was put off; it was too cold, even if they were healthy, Shyamma insisted. They spent the whole weekend indoors. Evan paced the small living room and stared out the window the way Maya used to when she was a child. Shyamma lay on the couch,

---

[4]**bacchi:** girl, daughter

reading magazines and marking all the things she would someday buy, when she had enough money. Her salary from the hospital was never quite enough; she was a woman with foreign syntax and got paid less than any man in the same position.

Such was Shyamma's freedom.

Later, in bed, Evan asked Maya again about the ski trip. His parents wanted to take them to Banff at Christmas, where a friend of theirs would let them stay for free.

"I don't think so."

Evan sat up and looked at her. Maya kept her eyes focussed on her book and remained slouched against the headboard.

"You always said you wanted—"

"I'm too old. Why don't you go without me?"

Evan ran his hand through his hair. He looked at her for a minute and then got out of bed.

"Fine. You figure out a way to tell my parents why you're not coming."

Evan, Maya had learned a long time ago, was uninterested in confrontation, in talking things through. He left the room and she heard him go into his study. He would work for the next few hours, slip into bed after she'd fallen asleep, and dream through the conflict. The next morning, he'd act as if nothing had been said, and by evening he'd be asking her the same question again. And if she did not give him the answer he wanted, the whole scene would repeat itself, day after day, until one of them—usually Maya—gave in.

She woke up early the next morning. Next to her, Evan slept soundly. Maya pushed his thin hair off his face and traced the outline of his ear, half willing him to wake up. He turned over to his other side, pulling the sheet with him. When she slid out of bed, he didn't move.

Down in the kitchen, watching the sky get lighter over the river, she smelled it, the dead fish smell. She sniffed the carton of cream, her fingers, the tail of her long braid. She opened the refrigerator, scanning the shelves for any forgotten beans, unwrapped meat or cheese. She pulled open the vegetable bin, checking for wilted broccoli, mushy tomatoes and soggy lettuce. She threw out some mouldy cottage cheese and a dried-up piece of fudge cake.

Maya's feet stuck to the kitchen floor as she scrubbed the cabinet doors.

"You are so ungrateful," Shyamma used to say, when Maya was sixteen and came home at two in the morning, smelling of alcohol and back seat sex.

Maya shrugged. It didn't matter what she did, Shyamma would be there. They were family, blood in a world of strangers. Like fish, they swam in the same school, a school of two, but a school nonetheless, dodging predators, careful of false bait.

Maya had finally bitten. Life with Evan was too tempting, an easy guarantee that she would not end up like Shyamma. But the ski trip weighed on her, pulling her in a direction she wasn't sure she wanted to go. Evan's parents had welcomed her as easily as they welcomed Shyamma; now she wished for a little resistance—a disapproving arched eyebrow or a look of confusion when they saw her living room, would have been good. Instead, Pat had smiled into the tiny mirrors, and Evy nodded as he eased himself in his old chair. She and Shyamma had done everything to make themselves acceptable, so why should the mixed decor worry the Everetts?

Maya brushed her teeth until her gums bled and the brush hurt her cheek. Once on a bus she saw a man scratching his arms with a steel pick comb, running it up and down his forearm, until the skin was raised in thin red welts and looked ready to burst.

"Heroin addict," Shyamma said, after the man stumbled off the bus.

"How do you know?"

"When they need a fix, they itch so bad, they want to jump out of their skin. That was him."

Looking at her reflection in the bathroom mirror, Maya felt the same way. She wanted to be out of this skin, out of this life and into another, one that fit her, not one that she had to fit.

That night, when Evan asked again, Maya said, "I don't want to go."

She lay in bed, flat on her back. Light from the house next door cut through the open blinds, striping the rumpled cotton sheets. She stared at the ceiling, searching for the fluorescent stars Evan had pasted on it when they first moved in.

Evan rolled over on his side, facing her. "If it's the money—"

"It's not the money."

"Then what is it?"

Maya flopped over, turning her back to him. "When I was a kid, all I ever wanted was to go on our school ski trips. Every year they had one, and all the cool people went. Those who couldn't afford it did cross-country on their own. Shyamma wouldn't even let me do that. When I said she didn't trust me to take care of myself, she said it was the cold—too cold for me. She really meant it was too cold for her."

"So here's your chance," Evan said.

"I don't care anymore. I can't do it."

"You won't even try."

She turned to face him. In the dark, she couldn't read his expression, but she resisted the urge to turn the light on.

"Why is it so important that I ski?"

Evan sighed. "You're part of the family."

"Ralph doesn't ski. He's still part of the family isn't he?" Evan's older brother-in-law refused to put on skis for political and economic reasons that the entire family teased him about.

"He's just scared."

"So? I bet Anne isn't forcing him to go to Banff."

"Jesus." Evan punched his pillow. "You're the one who wanted to go fishing, you wanted to ski, and now you're blaming me." He left the room, slamming the door behind him, and then slamming his study door as well.

Maybe she was scared. What if she couldn't really be an Everett? She was still horrified by her participation in the death of another creature. It was all very well to kill a fish on television or buy it at the store, nicely cleaned and filleted, but this—this was the beginning of a cycle she'd never be able to escape.

But what was the alternative? Maya lay on her back. On the ceiling, the stars glowed. There was the Big Dipper, the Little Dipper, Orion, the archer. Evan had followed the instructions so precisely, the whole sky filled their ceiling. When she initially suggested it, she'd thought of scattering them where she pleased. While she was out one day, Evan put them up, arranging each and every one just so.

When she showed her surprise, he frowned and said, "But that's how they're supposed to be. Every star in its place."

And where was hers? She had thought with Evan she would find it. But only if she forgot where she'd been before, and now she found that forgetting incomplete.

The next morning, Maya woke up at dawn and was on the road before the sun had completely risen. She didn't want to give herself the chance to change her mind and seeing Evan would have done that. She drove north on 79, past Mars, Moon Township, and the shrine in the median at Zelienople. A marker for someone who had died on the road, the small fir tree was decorated for July 4—red, white, and blue tinsel draped over it and an American flag languidly moving in the slipstream of the big trucks that roared by. At Easter, pastel-coloured plastic eggs hung from its branches, and at Christmas someone garnished it with bright ornaments, including a gold angel for the top. She'd seen similar shrines on the Mass Pike and the New Jersey Turnpike, so unusual they'd caught her eye.

By the time she pulled into Shyamma's neat little driveway, with the marigolds lined up on either side, it was well past eight o'clock. She knew that Shyamma would be in the kitchen. Maybe she could talk her into making some masala chai,[5] something to wash her mouth of the terrible McDonald's coffee she'd had an hour ago.

Shyamma didn't look up from the counter where she was rolling out some dough.

"Evan called. He wants to know if you'll be home for dinner."

Her tone was accusing, on Evan's behalf.

"I left him a note."

Shyamma tucked a strand of hair behind her ear. Her hair was still black and shiny, a testament to the coconut oil she used regularly and rigorous brushing. Her small brown face was slack at the jaw and under the chin, but her cheeks were high and firm, turning into small apples when she smiled. She had a sweet smile, Evan said, like Maya. But neither of them was smiling now.

"Paratha?"[6]

"Stuffed kulcha."[7] Shyamma kept rolling the small rounds of springy dough.

"For breakfast?" Maya was used to seeing the stuffed bread on special occasions only.

"No one here to tell me I can't."

She put the water to boil, in a saucepan, Maya noticed with relief. If Shyamma was making masala chai, Maya was not in that much trouble.

"I killed a fish." The words sounded terrible out loud, damning, yet she understood in that moment why criminals often confessed. A fleeting lightness lifted in her as she waited for her aunt's absolution.

"Did you eat it?"

"No." What did her aunt think she was? "I tried to save its life."

Shyamma added two teaspoons of tea to the boiling water and some milk. She let it boil vigorously, like the chai-wallahs[8] back home did, in huge pots on single burners.

"Sounds like a contradiction."

"It was an accident."

They ate in silence, at the same formica-topped table Shyamma had bought twenty years ago at a yard sale. The kulcha was slightly burnt, crispy at the edges and soft in the middle. Maya couldn't remember

---

[5]**masala chai:** a hot, spiced, milky tea
[6]**Paratha:** a flaky, fried bread, sometimes mixed or stuffed with other ingredients
[7]**kulcha:** a flatbread, sometimes stuffed with other ingredients
[8]**chai-wallahs:** roadside tea merchants

when it had tasted so good. "You don't have to come here every time you want a stuffed kulcha."

Shyamma cleared the dishes as she spoke. Maya had the impression she was going somewhere, that she didn't want her to stay.

"I know." She had the recipe, carefully pasted into a notebook with a number of other recipes Shyamma had insisted on showing her. At the time, she'd resisted; it seemed unnecessary, going back to a time when girls were prepared for marriage. Now she understood Shyamma had not been preparing her for anyone but herself.

As it turned out, Shyamma did have plans. She was going to a friend's house to discuss their Christmas vacation, a cruise somewhere warm and tropical. Maya hid her surprise; the only holidays her aunt had ever taken were their trips to India. Not wanting to even slightly dissuade her, Maya said nothing. She took the leftover kulcha and headed home, with promises to bring Evan back in a few weeks.

When she got home, Evan was out. She went straight to the bedroom and dug around for the leftover stars stashed in her bedside table. She cleared off the table and stood on it; using the wall for balance, she added her own star to the cluster directly above her side of the bed.

All these years, she thought the answer lay in teaching Shyamma to love the cold. Maybe she was wrong.

Maya sat on the porch staring across the river. The sun had nearly set and the air felt like rain, heavy and full of promise. Her skin was clammy from the heat and humidity, but it didn't bother her. It reminded her of the way she felt in the monsoon, just before the rains came, turning the streets into muddy rivers that came up to her knees.

The door opened, and she saw Evan's shadow cast down the stairs. He stood for a moment in the doorway, drinking a beer.

"Nice night," he said.

His voice was low and cautious as he sat down next to her. Maya couldn't bring herself to look at his face, that sweet combination of dimples and blue eyes that showed his confusion no matter how hard he tried to hide it. Instead, she looked at his feet, grimy from a barefoot summer, the toenails ridged and hard, dirt rimming the cuticles. Later, maybe, his nails would scratch dully against her legs, her ankles, and the tops of her feet, leaving white lines and marks across her own dry brown skin, never hard enough to draw blood, but enough to mark Evan on her.

Storytelling is the oldest form of education.

Terry Tempest Williams

"Shyamma used to have a small shrine in the corner of our kitchen." Her voice was hoarse from thirst and silence. "Incense, flowers, an old calendar painting of Ganesh.[9] That's all. Whenever I had friends over, I'd try to keep them from going in there."

"Why?"

"So I wouldn't have to hear them laugh and say, 'Ew, what's that?' and then explain why my aunt was worshipping a god with an elephant head."

"The god of all beginnings and the remover of obstacles." Evan sat down next to her.

"Shyamma told you that."

"When we got married."

Maya smiled. At the time, she would have forbidden the mention of Ganesh or any other god at her wedding, yet Shyamma had managed to find a space for him.

"I'm going to the temple when she comes."

One day, Shyamma will be gone, she thought, and I want to be left with more than the calendar image of a pot-bellied, elephant god.

He took her hand and squeezed it. "Want me to come?" "No. But no more fishing trips, okay?"

Maya drew a sip of beer from the long-necked bottle, letting a few drops drip down her chin. She held the cool glass against her temple and watched the lights come on across the river, solitary stars dotting a dark, lonely land. Evan put his hand on the back of her neck and stroked the damp hairs hanging out of her bun. They sat for a long time in silence, listening to the cicadas buzzing in the still heat, waiting for the storm to break and the sky to clear.

---

[9] **Ganesh:** an elephant-headed Hindu deity, remover of obstacles

Geeta Kothari's fiction and non-fiction have appeared in several anthologies and journals, such as the *Toronto South Asian Review,* the *New England Review,* the *Kenyon Review,* and *Her Mother's Ashes.* She is the editor of the anthology *Did My Mama Like to Dance? and Other Stories about Mothers and Daughters.*

I. Response

 a. Explain how the first paragraph symbolically captures one of the main themes of the story. Reread the story carefully, noting other passages or references that you think might have a symbolic meaning. Be prepared to present your ideas to a group or the class.

 b. Why does Maya both envy and resent Evan?

 c. Throughout her life, Maya has relied on others to give her a sense of direction. Give some specific examples. Do you think this is still true at the end of the story? Explain.

 d. What are some of the decisions Maya has to make in this story, and what choices are available to her? Do you think she makes good or bad decisions? Why?

 e. "The Spaces Between Stars" depicts a particular situation. Do you think the story has a broader relevance? Why?

 f. Discuss whether you were able to connect with the story, and whether that, in turn, affected your enjoyment of it.

2. Literature Studies *Story Endings* Some stories end with **closure**, while others are open-ended. What kind of ending does "The Spaces Between Stars" have? Give reasons for your answer, including specific references from the text. Is this a question that can be answered definitively? Why or why not?

Closure occurs when a story ends without ambiguity. The main crises and/or conflicts are neatly wrapped up and the reader has a sense that the story is truly finished. In an *open-ended story,* the reader is uncertain about what might happen next; several outcomes are possible.

---

3. Writing *Letter* Adopt the persona of Maya and compose the letter she would write to Evan's parents to explain her decision not to participate in the family skiing trip in Banff. Your writing should reflect your audience and purpose.

4. Critical Thinking In "The Spaces Between Stars," author Geeta Kothari explores some issues related to the mingling of different cultures. In a group, identify and discuss these issues. What are the main problems and challenges in Maya and Evan's marriage, and what solutions appear at the end of the story? Summarize your conclusions for the class.

The Chrysanthemums

by John Steinbeck

**Some people feel
a deep restlessness
for something
they can't quite name ...**

THE HIGH GREY-FLANNEL FOG OF WINTER CLOSED OFF the Salinas Valley[1] from the sky and from all the rest of the world. On every side it sat like a lid on the mountains and made of the great valley a closed pot. On the broad, level land floor the gang ploughs[2] bit deep and left the black earth shining like metal where the shares had cut. On the foot-hill ranches across the Salinas River, the yellow stubble fields seemed to be bathed in pale cold sunshine, but there was no sunshine in the valley now in December. The thick willow scrub along the river flamed with sharp and positive yellow leaves.

It was a time of quiet and of waiting. The air was cold and tender. A light wind blew up from the southwest so that the farmers were mildly hopeful of a good rain before long; but fog and rain do not go together.

Across the river, on Henry Allen's foot-hill ranch there was little work to be done, for the hay was cut and stored and the orchards were ploughed up to receive the rain deeply when it should come. The cattle on the higher slopes were becoming shaggy and rough-coated.

---

[1]**Salinas Valley:** a fertile valley of central California, about 30 km inland from the coast
[2]**gang ploughs:** a plough with several blades, making parallel furrows

Elisa Allen, working in her flower garden, looked down across the yard and saw Henry, her husband, talking to two men in business suits. The three of them stood by the tractor-shed, each man with one foot on the side of the little Fordson.[3] They smoked cigarettes and studied the machine as they talked.

Elisa watched them for a moment and then went back to her work. She was thirty-five. Her face was lean and strong and her eyes were as clear as water. Her figure looked blocked and heavy in her gardening costume, a man's black hat pulled low down over her eyes, clod-hopper shoes, a figured print dress almost completely covered by a big corduroy apron with four big pockets to hold the snips, the trowel and scratcher, the seeds and the knife she worked with. She wore heavy leather gloves to protect her hands while she worked.

She was cutting down the old year's chrysanthemum stalks with a pair of short and powerful scissors. She looked down toward the men by the tractor-shed now and then. Her face was eager and mature and handsome; even her work with the scissors was over-eager, over-powerful. The chrysanthemum stems seemed too small and easy for her energy.

She brushed a cloud of hair out of her eyes with the back of her glove, and left a smudge of earth on her cheek in doing it. Behind her stood the neat white farmhouse with red geraniums close-banked around it as high as the windows. It was a hard-swept-looking little house, with hard-polished windows, and a clean mud-mat on the front steps.

Elisa cast another glance toward the tractor-shed. The strangers were getting into their Ford coupé. She took off a glove and put her strong fingers down into the forest of new green chrysanthemum sprouts that were growing around the old roots. She spread the leaves and looked down among the close-growing stems. No aphids were there, no sow bugs or snails or cutworms. Her terrier fingers destroyed such pests before they could get started.

Elisa started at the sound of her husband's voice. He had come near quietly, and he leaned over the wire fence that protected her flower garden from cattle and dogs and chickens.

"At it again," he said. "You've got a strong new crop coming."

Elisa straightened her back and pulled on the gardening glove again. "Yes. They'll be strong this coming year." In her tone and on her face there was a little smugness.

"You've got a gift with things," Henry observed. "Some of those

---

[3]**Fordson:** a brand of tractor made by the Ford Motor Company

yellow chrysanthemums you had this year were ten inches across. I wish you'd work out in the orchard and raise some apples that big."

Her eyes sharpened. "Maybe I could do it, too. I've a gift with things, all right. My mother had it. She could stick anything in the ground and make it grow. She said it was having planters' hands that knew how to do it."

"Well, it sure works with flowers," he said.

"Henry, who were those men you were talking to?"

"Why, sure, that's what I came to tell you. They were from the Western Meat Company. I sold those thirty head of three-year-old steers. Got nearly my own price, too."

"Good," she said. "Good for you."

"And I thought," he continued, "I thought how it's Saturday afternoon, and we might go into Salinas for dinner at a restaurant, and then to a picture show—to celebrate, you see."

"Good," she repeated. "Oh, yes. That will be good."

Henry put on his joking tone. "There's fights tonight. How'd you like to go to the fights?"

"Oh, no," she said breathlessly. "No, I wouldn't like fights."

"Just fooling, Elisa. We'll go to a movie. Let's see. It's two now. I'm going to take Scotty and bring down those steers from the hill. It'll take us maybe two hours. We'll go in town about five and have dinner at the Cominos Hotel. Like that?"

"Of course I'll like it. It's good to eat away from home."

"All right, then. I'll go get up a couple of horses."

She said: "I'll have plenty of time to transplant some of these sets, I guess."

She heard her husband calling Scotty down by the barn. And a little later she saw the two men ride up the pale yellow hillside in search of the steers.

There was a little square sandy bed kept for rooting the chrysanthemums. With her trowel she turned the soil over and over, and smoothed it and patted it firm. Then she dug ten parallel trenches to receive the sets. Back at the chrysanthemum bed she pulled out the little crisp shoots, trimmed off the leaves of each one with her scissors and laid it on a small orderly pile.

A squeak of wheels and plod of hoofs came from the road. Elisa looked up. The country road ran along the dense bank of willows and cottonwoods that bordered the river, and up this road came a curious vehicle, curiously drawn. It was an old spring-wagon, with a round canvas top on it like the cover of a prairie schooner. It was drawn by an old bay horse and a little grey-and-white burro. A big, stubble-bearded man sat between the cover flaps and drove the crawling team. Underneath the wagon, between the hind wheels, a lean and rangy mongrel dog walked sedately. Words were painted on the canvas, in clumsy, crooked letters. "Pots, pans, knives, sisors, lawn mores, Fixed." Two rows of articles, and the triumphantly definitive "Fixed" below. The black paint had run down in little sharp points beneath each letter.

Elisa, squatting on the ground, watched to see the crazy, loose-jointed wagon pass by. But it didn't pass. It turned into the farm road in front of her house, crooked old wheels skirling[4] and squeaking. The rangy dog darted from between the wheels and ran ahead. Instantly the two ranch shepherds flew out at him. Then all three stopped, and with stiff and quivering tails, with taut straight legs, with ambassadorial dignity, they slowly circled, sniffing daintily. The caravan pulled up to Elisa's wire fence and stopped. Now the newcomer dog, feeling outnumbered, lowered his tail and retired under the wagon with raised hackles and bared teeth.

The man on the wagon seat called out: "That's a bad dog in a fight when he gets started."

Elisa laughed. "I see he is. How soon does he generally get started?"

The man caught up her laughter and echoed it heartily. "Sometimes not for weeks and weeks," he said. He climbed stiffly down, over the wheel. The horse and the donkey drooped like unwatered flowers.

Elisa saw that he was a very big man. Although his hair and beard were greying, he did not look old. His worn black suit was wrinkled and spotted with grease. The laughter had disappeared from his face and eyes the moment his laughing voice ceased. His eyes were dark, and they were full of the brooding that gets in the eyes of teamsters and of sailors. The calloused hands he rested on the wire fence were cracked, and every crack was a black line. He took off his battered hat.

"I'm off my general road, ma'am," he said. "Does this dirt road cut over across the river to the Los Angeles highway?"

Elisa stood up and shoved the thick scissors in her apron pocket. "Well, yes, it does, but it winds around and then fords the river. I don't think your team could pull through the sand."

He replied with some asperity: "It might surprise you what them beasts can pull through."

"When they get started?" she asked.

He smiled for a second. "Yes. When they get started."

"Well," said Elisa, "I think you'll save time if you go back to the Salinas road and pick up the highway there."

---

[4]**skirling:** a wailing sound, like that made by bagpipes

He drew a big finger down the chicken wire and made it sing. "I ain't in any hurry, ma'am. I go from Seattle to San Diego and back every year. Takes all my time. About six months each way. I aim to follow nice weather."

Elisa took off her gloves and stuffed them in her apron pocket with the scissors. She touched the under edge of her man's hat, searching for fugitive hairs. "That sounds like a nice kind of way to live," she said.

He leaned confidentially over the fence. "Maybe you noticed the writing on my wagon. I mend pots and sharpen knives and scissors. You got any of them things to do?"

"Oh, no," she said quickly. "Nothing like that." Her eyes hardened with resistance.

"Scissors is the worst thing," he explained. "Most people just ruin scissors trying to sharpen 'em, but I know how. I got a special tool. It's a little bobbit kind of thing, and patented. But it sure does the trick."

"No. My scissors are all sharp."

"All right, then. Take a pot," he continued earnestly, "a bent pot, or a pot with a hole. I can make it like new so you don't have to buy no new ones. That's a saving for you."

"No," she said shortly. "I tell you I have nothing like that for you to do."

His face fell to an exaggerated sadness. His voice took on a whining undertone. "I ain't had a thing to do today. Maybe I won't have no supper tonight. You see I'm off my regular road. I know folks on the highway clear from Seattle to San Diego. They save their things for me to sharpen up because they know I do it so good and save them money."

"I'm sorry," Elisa said irritably. "I haven't anything for you to do."

His eyes left her face and fell to searching the ground. They roamed about until they came to the chrysanthemum bed where she had been working. "What's them plants, ma'am?"

The irritation and resistance melted from Elisa's face. "Oh, those are chrysanthemums, giant whites and yellows. I raise them every year, bigger than anybody around here."

"Kind of a long-stemmed flower? Looks like a quick puff of colored smoke?" he asked.

"That's it. What a nice way to describe them."

"They smell kind of nasty till you get used to them," he said.

"It's a good bitter smell," she retorted, "not nasty at all."

He changed his tone quickly. "I like the smell myself."

"I had ten-inch blooms this year," she said.

The man leaned farther over the fence. "Look. I know a lady down the road a piece, has got the nicest garden you ever seen. Got nearly every kind of flower but no chrysanthemums. Last time I was mending a copper-bottom washtub for her (that's a hard job but I do it good), she said to me: 'If you ever run acrost some nice chrysanthemums I wish you'd try to get me a few seeds.' That's what she told me."

Elisa's eyes grew alert and eager. "She couldn't have known much about chrysanthemums. You *can* raise them from seed, but it's much easier to root the little sprouts you see there."

"Oh," he said. "I s'pose I can't take none to her, then."

"Why yes you can," Elisa cried. "I can put some in damp sand, and you can carry them right along with you. They'll take root in the pot if you keep them damp. And then she can transplant them."

"She'd sure like to have some, ma'am. You say they're nice ones?"

"Beautiful," she said. "Oh, beautiful." Her eyes shone. She tore off the battered hat and shook out her dark pretty hair. "I'll put them in a flowerpot, and you can take them right with you. Come into the yard."

While the man came through the picket gate Elisa ran excitedly along the geranium-bordered path to the back of the house. And she returned carrying a big red flower-pot. The gloves were forgotten now. She kneeled on the ground by the starting bed and dug up the sandy soil with her fingers and scooped it into the bright new flower-pot. Then she picked up the little pile of shoots she had prepared. With her strong fingers she pressed them into the sand and tamped around them with her knuckles. The man stood over her. "I'll tell you what to do," she said. "You remember so you can tell the lady."

"Yes, I'll try to remember."

"Well, look. These will take root in about a month. Then she must set them out, about a foot apart in good rich earth like this, see?" She lifted a handful of dark soil for him to look at. "They'll grow fast and tall. Now remember this: In July tell her to cut them down, about eight inches from the ground."

"Before they bloom?" he asked.

"Yes, before they bloom." Her face was tight with eagerness. "They'll grow right up again. About the last of September the buds will start."

She stopped and seemed perplexed. "It's the budding that takes the most care," she said hesitantly. "I don't know how to tell you." She looked deep into his eyes, searchingly. Her mouth opened a little, and she seemed to be listening. "I'll try to tell you," she said. "Did you ever hear of planting hands?"

"Can't say I have, ma'am."

"Well, I can only tell you what it feels like. It's when you're picking off the buds you don't want. Everything goes right down into your fingertips. You watch your fingers work. They do it themselves. You can feel how it is. They pick and pick the buds. They never make a mistake. They're with the plant. Do you see? Your fingers and the plant. You can feel that, right up your arm. They know. They never make a mistake. You can feel it. When you're like that you can't do anything wrong. Do you see that? Can you understand that?"

She was kneeling on the ground looking up at him. Her breast swelled passionately.

The man's eyes narrowed. He looked away self-consciously. "Maybe I know," he said. "Sometimes in the night in the wagon there—"

Elisa's voice grew husky. She broke in on him: "I've never lived as you do, but I know what you mean. When the night is dark—why, the stars are sharp-pointed, and there's quiet. Why, you rise up and up! Every pointed star gets driven into your body. It's like that. Hot and sharp and—lovely."

Kneeling there, her hand went out toward his legs in the greasy black trousers. Her hesitant fingers almost touched the cloth. Then her hand dropped to the ground. She crouched low like a fawning dog.

He said: "It's nice, just like you say. Only when you don't have no dinner, it ain't."

She stood up then, very straight, and her face was ashamed. She held the flower-pot out to him and placed it gently in his arms. "Here. Put it in your wagon, on the seat, where you can watch it. Maybe I can find something for you to do."

At the back of the house she dug in the can pile and found two old and battered aluminum saucepans. She carried them back and gave them to him. "Here, maybe you can fix these."

His manner changed. He became professional. "Good as new I can fix them." At the back of his wagon he set a little anvil, and out of an oily tool-box dug a small machine hammer. Elisa came through the gate to watch him while he pounded out the dents in the kettles. His mouth grew sure and knowing. At a difficult part of the work he sucked his underlip.

"You sleep right in the wagon?" Elisa asked.

"Right in the wagon, ma'am. Rain or shine I'm dry as a cow in there."

"It must be nice," she said. "It must be very nice. I wish women could do such things."

"It ain't the right kind of a life for a woman."

Her upper lip raised a little, showing her teeth. "How do you know?

How can you tell?" she said.

"I don't know, ma'am," he protested. "Of course I don't know. Now here's your kettles, done. You don't have to buy no new ones."

"How much?"

"Oh, fifty cents'll do. I keep my prices down and my work good. That's why I have all them satisfied customers up and down the high-way."

Elisa brought him a fifty-cent piece from the house and dropped it in his hand. "You might be surprised to have a rival some time. I can sharpen scissors, too. And I can beat the dents out of little pots. I could show you what a woman might do."

He put his hammer back in the oily box and shoved the little anvil out of sight. "It would be a lonely life for a woman, ma'am, and a scarey life, too, with animals creeping under the wagon all night." He climbed over the single-tree[5] steadying himself with a hand on the burro's white rump. He settled himself in the seat, picked up the lines. "Thank you kindly ma'am," he said. "I'll do like you told me; I'll go back and catch the Salinas road."

"Mind," she called, "if you're long in getting there, keep the sand damp."

"Sand, ma'am? ... Sand? Oh, sure. You mean around the chrysan-themums. Sure I will." He clucked his tongue. The beasts leaned lux-uriously into their collars. The mongrel dog took his place between the back wheels. The wagon turned and crawled out the entrance road and back the way it had come, along the river.

Elisa stood in front of her wire fence watching the slow progress of the caravan. Her shoulders were straight, her head thrown back, her eyes half-closed, so that the scene came vaguely into them. Her lips moved silently, forming the words "Good-bye—good-bye." Then she whispered: "That's a bright direction. There's a glowing there." The sound of her whisper startled her. She shook herself free and looked about to see whether anyone had been listening. Only the dogs had heard. They lifted their heads toward her from their sleeping in the dust, and then stretched out their chins and settled asleep again. Elisa turned and ran hurriedly into the house.

In the kitchen she reached behind the stove and felt the water tank. It was full of hot water from the noonday cooking. In the bath-room she tore off her soiled clothes and flung them into the corner. And then she scrubbed herself with a little block of pumice, legs and thighs, loins and chest and arms, until her skin was scratched and red. When

---

⁵single-tree: the crossbar used to hitch a horse to a wagon or other vehicle

she dried herself she stood in front of a mirror in her bedroom and looked at her body. She tightened her stomach and threw out her chest. She turned and looked over her shoulder at her back.

After a while she began to dress, slowly. She put on her newest underclothing and her nicest stockings and the dress which was the symbol of her prettiness. She worked carefully on her hair, pencilled her eyebrows and rouged her lips.

Before she was finished she heard the little thunder of hoofs and the shouts of Henry and his helper as they drove the red steers into the corral. She heard the gate bang shut and set herself for Henry's arrival.

His step sounded on the porch. He entered the house calling: "Elisa, where are you?"

"In my room, dressing. I'm not ready. There's hot water for your bath. Hurry up. It's getting late."

When she heard him splashing in the tub, Elisa laid his dark suit on the bed, and shirt and socks and tie beside it. She stood his polished shoes on the floor beside the bed. Then she went to the porch and sat primly and stiffly down. She looked toward the river road where the willow-line was still yellow with frosted leaves so that under the high grey fog they seemed a thin band of sunshine. This was the only color in the grey afternoon. She sat unmoving for a long time. Her eyes blinked rarely.

Henry came banging out of the door, shoving his tie inside his vest as he came. Elisa stiffened and her face grew tight. Henry stopped short and looked at her. "Why—why, Elisa. You look so nice!"

"Nice? You think I look nice? What do you mean by 'nice'?"

Henry blundered on. "I don't know. I mean you look different, strong and happy."

"I am strong? Yes, strong. What do you mean 'strong'?"

He looked bewildered. "You're playing some kind of a game," he said helplessly. "It's a kind of play. You look strong enough to break a calf over your knee, happy enough to eat it like a watermelon."

For a second she lost her rigidity. "Henry! Don't talk like that. You didn't know what you said." She grew complete again. "I'm strong," she boasted. "I never knew before how strong."

Henry looked down toward the tractor-shed, and when he brought his eyes back to her, they were his own again. "I'll get out the car. You can put on your coat while I'm starting."

Elisa went into the house. She heard him drive to the gate and idle down his motor, and then she took a long time to put on her hat. She pulled it here and pressed it there. When Henry turned the motor off she slipped into her coat and went out.

The little roadster bounced along on the dirt road by the river, raising the birds and driving the rabbits into the brush. Two cranes flapped heavily over the willow-line and dropped into the riverbed.

Far ahead on the road Elisa saw a dark speck. She knew.

She tried not to look as they passed it, but her eyes would not obey. She whispered to herself sadly: "He might have thrown them off the road. That wouldn't have been much trouble, not very much. But he kept the pot," she explained. "He had to keep the pot. That's why he couldn't get them off the road."

The roadster turned a bend and she saw the caravan ahead. She swung full around toward her husband so she could not see the little covered wagon and the mis-matched team as the car passed them.

In a moment it was over. The thing was done. She did not look back.

She said loudly, to be heard above the motor: "It will be good, tonight, a good dinner."

"Now you've changed again," Henry complained. He took one hand from the wheel and patted her knee. "I ought to take you in to dinner oftener. It would be good for both of us. We get so heavy out on the ranch."

"Henry," she asked, "could we have wine at dinner?"

"Sure we could. Say! That will be fine."

She was silent for a while; then she said: "Henry, at those prize-fights, do the men hurt each other very much?"

"Sometimes a little, not often. Why?"

"Well, I've read how they break noses, and blood runs down their chests. I've read how the fighting gloves get heavy and soggy with blood."

He looked round at her. "What's the matter, Elisa? I didn't know you read things like that." He brought the car to a stop, then turned to the right over the Salinas River bridge.

"Do any women ever go to the fights?" she asked.

"Oh, sure, some. What's the matter, Elisa. Do you want to go? I don't think you'd like it, but I'll take you if you really want to go."

She relaxed limply in the seat. "Oh, no. No. I don't want to go. I'm sure I don't." Her face was turned away from him. "It will be enough if we can have wine. It will be plenty." She turned up her coat collar so he could not see that she was crying weakly—like an old woman. ❯

> Not that the story need be long, but it will take
> a long while to make it short.
>
> Henry David Thoreau

John Steinbeck was born in Salinas, California, in 1902.
He was educated at Stanford University and worked as a fruit
picker and ranch hand. His most well-known book,
The Grapes of Wrath, won a Pulitzer Prize in 1940. Steinbeck
won the Nobel Prize for literature in 1962. His works include
*Tortilla Flat, Of Mice and Men, The Moon Is Down, Cannery
Row, East of Eden,* and *The Winter of Our Discontent.* He also
wrote an autobiographical account of a trip across the U.S.
with his pet poodle, called *Travels With Charley.* A number
of his books have been made into films.

1. *Response*

a. When and where do you think "The Chrysanthemums"
takes place? List specific phrases and words that help to
establish the setting.

b. What was your initial reaction to Elisa? Did your impression change as the story progressed?

c. Explain the way in which the peddler manages to capture
Elisa's attention and then nudge her into giving him a job.
What can you infer about the peddler's character from this
behaviour?

d. At the end of the story, why do you think Elisa first shows
interest in the fights, then adamantly changes her mind?

e. What significance do the chrysanthemums have for Elisa?
For Henry? For the peddler? Comment on whether Steinbeck
chose an appropriate title for the story.

2. *Oral Language* *Group Discussion* "'I've never lived as you do,
but I know what you mean. When the night is dark—why the
stars are sharp-pointed, and there's quiet. Why, you rise up
and up! Every pointed star gets driven into your body. It's like
that. Hot and sharp and—lovely.'" In a group, discuss what
Elisa means. Do you think the peddler knows, or cares, what
she is saying? What do you think Elisa is revealing about
herself? Have one group member present your group's
conclusions to the class.

3. **Literature Studies** *Juxtaposition* Steinbeck uses **juxtaposition** to develop a contradictory impression of Elisa's character. Reread the story, noting the places where Elisa seems to be bold and confident, as well as the places where she seems tentative. Record your observations in a T-chart format, using specific references from the story. How is this juxtaposition related to the central ideas in the story? Would you describe Elisa as predominantly a strong or weak person? Give reasons for your answer.

Juxtaposition is the intentional placement of dissimilar words or ideas side by side for a particular purpose—to emphasize contrasting ideas, for example.

4. **Writing** *Point of View* Steinbeck has used the third-person limited point of view to tell this story from Elisa's perspective. Using the same time frame and setting, write an alternative version of the story from Henry or the peddler's point of view. Be prepared to explain the reasons behind any changes you make to the story.

5. **Focus on Context** John Steinbeck wrote a number of novels and short stories set in the Salinas Valley of California—an area he knew from his own life. What conclusions can you draw from "The Chrysanthemums" about life in this region, especially for women? Read one other Steinbeck work set in this region, such as a short story from *The Pastures of Heaven* or an episode from *The Grapes of Wrath*, for example. Write a brief essay (one or two pages), in which you investigate the similarities and differences in the themes and situations portrayed in "The Chrysanthemums" and the other work you have read.

Theme Connections

- *"Touching Bottom," a story in which a character explores her fears and strengths, Vol. I, p. 124*
- *"There's Silence Between One Page and Another," a poem in which the speaker lacks confidence in making some decisions, Vol. I, p. 183*
- *"A New Perspective," an essay about seeing a family relationship from a new perspective, page Vol. II, p. 45*
- *"That's Extraordinary!" a radio play in which one character manipulates another, Vol. II, p. 179*

Touching Bottom

by Kari Strutt

"How many fingers?" Dad asked at bath time.

I was afraid, but I ducked my head into the half-full white tub. I opened my eyes, then came up sputtering.

"Two."

"That's right." Then his hand, broad as a rainbow, covered my head all the way to my ears, and slicked back my sopping hair. He wrapped me in a clean yellow towel, and the fear, what was left of it, evaporated.

I could open my eyes under water.

The summer I turned seven I went to Camp Kinaird with fifty other girls. "Where young girls learn to swim," Dad quoted from the black text between the brochure photos of smiling kids.

"You should learn to swim," he said, "you never know when you'll end up in water that's over your head."

The camp instructors told me I was a good swimmer. My spindly arms cut the water like fins, and I could circle them at a furious pace. I learned to put my face in the water, turn my head for air. I was quick, like a water beetle, and I liked the feeling of the cool water pushing through my hair.

On the fifth day of swim lessons, the fat girl came to shore with a dark glistening streak on her back. Somebody shrieked, "You gotta leech on you," and the shoreline became a seething mass of squealing, blue-lipped girls. The terror rang in my ears long after the camp counsellor salted the girl's back and caught the writhing leech in an old tin can. She was still whimpering when we went to the cookhouse for lunch.

For the rest of the summer I refused to go in the water. The other girls backstroked and side stroked and perfected their Australian crawls. The fat girl and I sat on the dock watching a black bloodsucker make its way across a yellow plastic bowl lodged in the sandy bottom near shore.

That fall my Dad signed me up for Red Cross swimming lessons. In a pool.

"You can start again," Dad said. "I'm sure there are no leeches at the YMCA, but I'll come and watch, just to be sure."

When we got to the YMCA, Dad and I walked around the pool together, looking for leeches. I thought I saw one, but it was just a Band-Aid.

The pool water was clear blue-green and with my goggles on I could see the bottom. There were wide black lines painted along the length of it. I used the lines to make sure I was swimming straight. I finished all of the Red Cross lessons, then I joined a swim club and learned to race. I trained every day, back and forth in the pool, guided on either side by the lane markers—bright strings of plastic bubbles, led from below by the thick black lines. When I turned fourteen I trained twice a day, every morning at five-thirty and every evening at five. Dad drove me to practice after practice, day after day, year after year.

I was skinny and hungry all the time. I ate a lot, but it was never enough. Sometimes I swam the backstroke, staring at the pool ceiling and dreaming of macaroni and cheese. After practice I sliced wafers of cold butter, let them melt on my tongue.

I learned to swim a long ways, but I never did get comfortable in murky water: lakes, rivers, anywhere I couldn't see bottom. That kind of water made my throat open too wide to bring the air into my lungs, made me breathe fast, out of control.

That's why, when I think of California, I get queasy. I lived there for four years with my husband. He came to Canada on business, to the art gallery where I worked, and swept me away to Los Angeles on a blue wave of charm.

My Dad told me not to go, not to marry him. He said I would be sorry. He said, "His mid-life crisis will pass soon enough and you'll be stuck in California, like a fish out of water." He said he would not come to the wedding. He didn't. The day I got married I felt lonely and afraid.

I lived with my husband, my sister-in-law and Ian, in a house in the San Fernando Valley. The air is close in that valley, but the people are distant, separated from each other by car lengths and private desires.

My husband's sister was a loveless woman, no girlfriends and no boyfriends. She once called the police when she found a rat in the kitchen. She screamed into the phone, "He's in the house! He's in the house!"

"Where in the house?" they demanded.

"He's under the stove," she shrieked. When the 9-1-1 operators found out she was talking about a rat and not a violent perpetrator, they hung up on her. She stood on the front porch for four hours, sweat trickling into the small of her back, waiting for help that never arrived. After that, she refused to cook.

Ian was my husband's son from a previous marriage. The summer Ian was born, I got a new CCM bicycle and I built a tree fort with my friend Elaine.

Ian was a sensible boy, tall for his age. I weighed more than he did, but our eyes were level. We listened to music. I introduced him to albums he'd never heard before: the Roches, Penguin Café Orchestra and Philip Glass. We laughed at the same movies. *Better Off Dead, Buckaroo Banzai, Real Genius, The Big Snit*. Ian was a good kid, smart.

Ian's mom told me once, "Don't try to be his mother; he already has one." She was taking Ian away for the weekend and I was seeing him out the door, making sure he had pajamas and enough underwear. I didn't want to be his mother, I just wanted her to know that I was good to him.

One day, Ian, my husband and I went to the beach near the Santa Monica pier. It was a warm day and the Santa Ana winds whipped the water into frothy whitecaps.

Ian was frantic about swimming, desperate to be in the water. I didn't really want to go because of the kind of water it was. Murky. I said yes anyway because his father wouldn't go with him, and kids should have fun. I told him, "I'll swim with you, but not where it's over our heads."

Ian was not a good swimmer, but good enough to do a few lengths. We stayed close to shore and let the waves knock us over. I laughed because Ian was laughing and whooping. His happiness caught me by the arm and spun me around, breathless and grinning. Ian could do that to me.

He bounced up and down in the waist-deep water. "Look at that," he said, pointing a slender arm, scraped at the elbow, toward the open water. "That's so awesome." There were boys on belly boards, fifty yards out, catching the bigger waves.

"Let's go there," Ian said. "It's not that deep and the waves are better. Can we?"

"Nope." I shook my head and his smile faded. I grabbed his waist and tickled him, extracting more laughter and a desperate squirm. Kissed the top of his head, the smell of salt and sunshine.

"Please, please, can we go? I'll stay right beside you. Please?"

I didn't like the idea, but he was right about the waves.

I told him we had to go a little further up the beach, because I didn't want the belly boarders to run us over. We went south, down the shore, not more than thirty yards or so, wading into chest-high water until, clear of the boarders, we stopped to rest. We put our backs to the incoming waves, watched a gull rise and drift north.

I could see Ian's father on the beach. He was lying in the sand, pretending not to watch the bronzed, blonde girls playing beach volleyball. He was lying on his stomach, hiding his pot belly from the sun and from their view.

Ian and I started swimming out to the bigger waves, and everything seemed okay. It's hard to tell where you are in the ocean, no lane markers, no bottom lines.

I was swimming and wondering if, in California, it was okay for a married man to lie on the beach watching girls while his second wife entertained his son.

That's when I noticed Ian and I were being pulled out to sea. We'd taken only a few strokes, but we were nearly as far from shore as the boarders. A few seconds later, we passed them.

Ian didn't notice.

He kept swimming until I said, "Ian. Stop. Stand up."

I dropped my feet to bottom and felt my toes dragging through the sand, just briefly. Then the bottom dropped away and the water was over my head.

"Head back to shore, Ian," I called. A hollowness was opening in my throat. Ian turned around without argument.

"You're going to have to swim hard," I said. "We're in some kind of current."

Ian swam hard. I swam behind him, pushing him forward by the soles of his feet. I could see the boarders, forward, to our left. We swam for a long time. We didn't get any closer.

My husband was a dark mark on the beach. He seemed to be talking to one of the volleyball players. I could see her pale yellow hair. She was standing above him; hands on hips. He was sitting in the sand, legs bundled to chest. I buried my face in the water, swam hard for shore.

Ian's front crawl grew lame. He was breathing loud and fast, exhaling twice with every stroke. He couldn't drag his arms out of the water.

"Keep swimming, Ian," I growled.

"I can't."

"You have to."

Ian kept swimming. He knew we were in trouble.

I thought about jellyfish stings and, just once, leeches, breathed slowly, looked toward the beach. The volleyball girl was sitting by my husband; they sat face to face, laughing.

Ian started to cry.

"I have a cramp in my calf," he said.

I know how bad that can be, like a rod of hot iron right through the belly of the muscle.

"Float on your back for a while."

Ian tried, but the waves kept washing into his mouth, making him cough, weak and watery.

I lifted Ian's head out of the water and held it up, side stroking in the direction of shore. Not losing ground, not gaining ground, stroke after stroke. Something in my shoulder snapped, and the joint began to grind. My sides clenched in the first spasms of exhaustion. I tried to add it up. Nearly half an hour of swimming in place, fifteen minutes of pulling Ian. That was equivalent to three miles at least, so I still had two more miles left in me, maybe three.

I felt dizzy. The water felt so cold now.

I wanted to let Ian go. I could see his father, reaching to touch the bronze girl.

"Can you try again, Ian? Just swim for a minute."

"No, I'm too tired."

"Just try, for me."

I didn't wait for him to answer, I just let him go. I knew instantly that it was a mistake. He started to drift away from me, seaward. I watched the distance between us grow until he screamed.

"Mom, help."

"You can shave four seconds off your best one hundred-yard time if you pull harder. Slow your cadence, and pull like this."

"Okay, coach."

I pulled hard, body rigid, head down, breaking the waves. A sprint, anaerobic, no time to breathe, no need to breathe. But when I got there, Ian was already going under, his face distorted by panic. He grabbed onto me, snarled my limbs with his. He was trying to keep his head above water and he pushed me under. He held me there, and for a few seconds I waited, hoping he would settle. When I started to run out of air, I pulled myself downward, away from him, deeper into the water.

It surprised me when my toes hit the sand. The bottom had never been too far away, twelve or fifteen feet at most, the water not much deeper than the diving tank at the YMCA. I opened my eyes and looked up. The water felt quiet. I could see Ian, above me, silhouetted against the yellow ball of the sun. I was so tired, and it was so soft and warm under that deep blanket of water. I thought I would sleep, just for a minute or two, collect my strength for the swim back to shore. Already dreaming, my knees touched coarse sand.

Kitchen table. Cinnamon toast.

"How come I didn't win, Dad?"

"Did you do your best?" Melted butter and spiced sugar, turning liquid on my tongue.

"Yes."

Dad's eyes, wise, weariness in the corners. "To win, you have to give until it hurts, then give some more."

On the surface of the water, Ian was still. My chest roared hot. I pushed myself upward, off the bottom, toward the pale light and the dark shadow of a boy.

At surface, I dragged air into aching lungs.

Ian on his back. Floating.

"I thought you might be dead," he said almost matter-of-factly. "I did like you told me, I'm floating." His body convulsed with uncontrollable shivers.

"I'm sorry, Ian. I won't let you go again."

I lay on my back, and cradled Ian's head on my chest. I thought that if I could swim north, get closer to the boarders, I could yell for help. I kicked us northward, parallel to the beach.

I know about the currents now. Bands, sometimes as narrow as twenty or thirty feet across, that pull toward deeper water. Swim parallel to shore and you can be free of them in a minute. Swim toward shore and you battle the current until you die.

I kicked and looked at the sky. I breathed slowly. I kicked and kicked until both calves locked into tight balls. Lungs felt so hot, so full.

I thought of the distance swimmer I once saw on television. The TV crew filmed her as she swam from Cuba to Florida, a boat beside her, keeping pace. The boat supported a moving net, a box of iron mesh to keep away sharks and jellyfish. It must have been nice, that net. She would always know she was in the right place, in miles of open water, even without any bottom lines.

Ian was quiet, resting. His shivering had nearly stopped. It sounded like he was humming. I had the smell of macaroni and cheese in my nostrils, the taste of slick, warm butter on my tongue.

I lay on my back, kicking, pulling weakly at the water with one arm. I hadn't looked around for a while, maybe ten or fifteen minutes, but suddenly I could hear the boarders.

"Ian, can you swim for a second?"

"I don't think so."

I held Ian upright with one arm and turned onto my stomach. We nearly ran into a blond boy, perhaps fifteen.

"Please," I asked, "My son is exhausted. Can I use your board to tow him to shore?"

The boy said nothing, but piloted his board to me. He helped me heave Ian onto the board and together we towed it to shore.

As we made our way in, I could see my husband, his hand on the waist of the bronze girl, sliding it slowly over the slick skin of her belly toward her breast. She brushed his hand, in that "somebody might be watching" kind of way. Her bikini had a pattern of teddy bears on it.

When we got to shore, I thanked the blond boy. Then I threw up in the sand. Mostly salt water. I retched for a long time after my stomach was empty. There were wide bleeding welts on my arms and back, and one eye was swollen shut. My right shoulder felt splintered inside.

Ian sat with me and covered his ears with his hands as my stomach heaved again. He looked at my bleeding arms. "I did that, didn't I?" I nodded. He cried, and that hurt worse than the welts or my eye.

"Should I get my dad?" he asked.

I wheezed a shallow "Yes."

Ian stumbled away from me and came back a few minutes later with a towel. "Dad's busy right now. He said he'll be here in a minute. Are you okay? Are you going to throw up again?"

"I don't think so." The taste of bitter bile on my teeth and gums.

"Good." He plopped into the sand and took my hand. We huddled together and I wrapped the beach towel around us, held Ian close, our cool skin touching, warming. We sat, silent, watching the waves tumble onto the sand.

Three months later I divorced Ian's father. I wasn't allowed to see Ian any more. I came home.

Ian is a man now. Last year he came to visit me, all the way from California. He is tall, and handsome, and very smart. We went for long walks and sang all the old songs we could remember: *Cats*, The Roches, *Songs from Liquid Days*. We talked about when we lived together, about

Disneyland, and Magic Mountain and shopping at the Galleria. We talked about what he would do when he finished college, his career as a photographer, his desire to move to London. He told me about a girl he had fallen in love with, how she had broken his heart. He said nothing of his father. I didn't ask.

The day before he went back to California, Ian took my biggest yellow towel, rolled his bathing suit and a pair of goggles inside it, and drove me to the public swimming pool near my house. I watched him doing lengths from a seat in the gallery. He is a powerful swimmer now, with a broad back, strong limbs and a well-tuned front crawl. He raced in high school. "Like you did," he smiled, "but probably a lot faster."

I asked him that night, after dinner, if he ever swam in the water off the coast.

He swirled his fingertip in a drizzle of cheese sauce that edged his plate. "Only when I have to," he replied, licking his finger clean. "I don't like the ocean much. But if I ever have kids, I'll make sure they learn how to swim in surf. I'll make sure they know about the currents."

After breakfast the next morning Ian flew to California. I drove back to the pool.

The water is different now.

"Government legislation and chlorine restrictions," the lifeguard said, slapping a grey mop onto the white deck. "The public pools have all been retrofitted for salt water." He swabbed limply. "Just as sterile, and better for the environment."

The salt muddied the blue-green water, made it less clear. The lines on the bottom were blurry, even with goggles. But salt in the water makes a swimmer buoyant. I floated easily.

I swam a few slow miles. Moving like a kayak. Felt the simple pull of each arm, the smooth thrust forward, my head slicing the water like a prow, my spine, compressed by gravity, elongating. I watched the dark mass of my own shadow on the pool bottom follow me from end to end. I swam and swam until the nagging hunger returned; then I let it sit there, familiar.

A lukewarm shower in a cold locker room. I carefully dried myself with a clean towel, fresh from the dryer. I drenched my salt-parched skin with lotion, sweet-scented with orange and ylang[1] to protect it from the harsh, dry cold of autumn.

I can still swim quite a ways. ❯

---

¹ylang: a scented oil derived from flowers

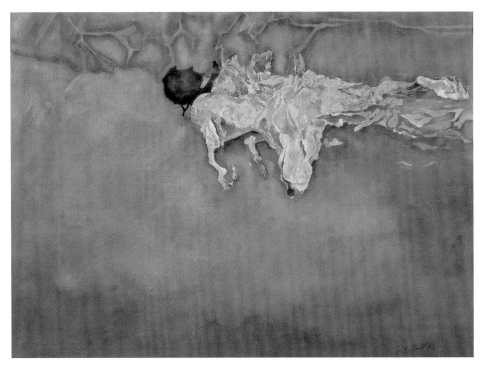

Swimmer in Yellow by Gareth Lloyd.

What techniques has the artist used to make *Swimmer in Yellow* visually interesting? Would you describe this work as a realistic painting? Explain your response, referring to specific elements of the painting.

Kari Strutt writes fiction and technical manuals. She lives in Calgary and is currently working on her first novel.

1. *Response*

a. The story begins with a retelling of some of the narrator's childhood memories. Is this an effective opening for a short story? Why or why not?

b. In your opinion, would this story be as effective if it were told in third-person narration? Explain.

c. Look for passages appearing in *italics*. What is different about these passages, and what functions do they serve?

d. What conflicts and complications are present in "Touching Bottom"? Describe the qualities that help the narrator to resolve these conflicts. Then, in a brief piece of personal writing, tell about a time when you needed the same qualities yourself.

e. What are some of the ways in which the narrator and Ian affected one another's lives? Support your opinion.

2. *Literature Studies* *Unifying Device* Describe the way in which Kari Strutt has used swimming as a **unifying device** within her story, from title to closing line. What are the most important narrative strands that are woven together? How does swimming function as a symbol, and what are the different meanings of the phrase "touching bottom"? Explain your ideas in a small group discussion.

A **unifying device** connects different parts of a narrative. It can be a metaphor, a symbol, an image, a character, or even an important word or phrase.

3. *Drama* *Reader's Theatre* In a group, prepare and perform a Reader's Theatre version of "Touching Bottom." In Reader's Theatre, the emphasis is on an expressive reading of narration and dialogue. Although physical movement is minimal, you may enhance the presentation with lighting, sound effects, or music. You may also edit the story somewhat to reduce the amount of narration.

4. *Language Conventions* *Pace and Flow* Using quotations from the story, show how Strutt uses sentence structure, punctuation, and paragraph breaks to shape the pace and flow of the story. For each example you choose, describe its important features (for example, comma use to break the sentence into short phrases) and then explain how those features influence the reader. Do you think the author does a good job of controlling the pace and flow of the story? Explain.

"Train rides seemed to open up an unused store of associations, provoking vivid flashes of remembered sight."

The Forest of Arden

by Hannah Grant

PAUL WAS DREAMING OF A WOMAN STANDING IN A FIELD with a gun. At first she was a small silhouette against a pinkish dawn sky, smudged by dirt on the train window. She grew larger and more distinct; he could see she wore rubber boots and a coat over a loose dress or nightgown. She held the rifle loosely, all her attention apparently focused on something beyond the train or invisible to Paul. As the field and the woman rushed towards him, he tried to determine whether she was actually moving; just before the train brought them parallel, she vanished in a blur of speed and he woke up.

The vibration of the train became the roar of a passing car. He smelled exhaust in the cool air blowing in from the window; somewhere down the street a child was crying. Faint music from the next room meant that Gabriel was up and working. Paul groped for the bedside clock and guessed seven thirty-two or -three; untangling his legs from the sheets, he put his feet on the floor. He no longer considered the extra few minutes of sleepy half-consciousness he had enjoyed as a child, but for a moment he sat on the edge of the bed, rubbing both hands across his face, then stood up and walked out of his room. The hall smelled of beer and laundry soap; he leaned against the bathroom doorframe and reached sideways to turn both taps on full. There was no need to hurry; he would have plenty of time to catch the train.

The derailment which blinded Paul in the summer of his eighth birthday happened during his first train ride. Chance placed him in one of the two cars which were severely damaged. After spending the afternoon of the first day in the observation car, and the night with his family, he had finally decided to explore the front of the train. He was caught standing in the aisle, surrounded by strangers, when the wave of force tossed him sideways into a confusion of soft bodies and breaking glass. He remembered a prolonged shriek, and a shock which he could not remember either fading or ending. After that, of course, there was only darkness.

Paul stepped out of the bathroom just as Gabriel's radio erupted into the rest of the apartment, blasting out a Renaissance dance tune. Paul found Gabriel's relationship to music one of his most endearing qualities as a roommate. He produced it naturally or artificially wherever he went: he splashed and sang while washing; talked back to radio and television; cursed and laughed out loud; walked heavily, whistled, hummed. Sometimes he sang in his sleep. Paul could follow Gabriel's every movement through the apartment, calculate his mood, even recognize his voice from the other side of a concert hall.

Just now Gabriel was singing loudly, if incoherently, along with a soft drum rhythm, obscuring both the main recorder and harpsichord parts. The irregularities of his voice were echoed by the impact of his steps, and Paul kept a prudent distance as he followed the carolling, dancing Gabriel towards the kitchen. He reached the doorframe just as the exaggerated percussion of the finale was punctuated by the creak of the opening refrigerator.

"Hell, there's no milk!"

"Third shelf, behind two jars. Good morning."

Gabriel swore appreciatively. A second, slower tune began pouring in from the hall. Paul found the kettle, filled it and plugged it in; he found a cup, the instant coffee, a spoon and his chair. He let the music completely erase the echoes of the dream, the melody gradually replacing the almost subliminal memory of the sound of the train.

After the accident, the effects of concussion swept over him in waves, pulling him in and out of a coma for two days. He had so strongly associated the return of consciousness with the return of vision that later, trying to remember, he found it difficult to distinguish between this time and many of the days following. Once he had learned to identify his waking hours by the hiss of the air conditioner and the pain in his arm, he began to connect sight with his return home. He moved into his family's new house in the city with only the uncertain recollection of a photograph of the front of a building. For several years afterwards, it seemed to him at times that he had never really woken up and never gone home.

All at once the kettle began to whistle and the telephone rang; a split second later, whistle, recorder and harpsichord were overpowered by an eerie strain of East Indian sitar.[1] From the hall, Gabriel's voice claimed emphatically that he was not at home, while the real Gabriel knocked over his chair and barged across the kitchen, shouting at the telephone. Paul heard the sitar stop in mid-whine as Gabriel began an energetic monologue in French. After an equally incomprehensible shout of farewell, Paul heard the clatter of the hall closet opening and the front door slamming closed. Gabriel's footsteps on the metal stairwell clanged into silence like distant bells.

Gabriel, a graduate engineer, was now majoring in theatre arts; he had a vast, incompatible collection of acquaintances who appeared periodically and left obscure messages on his answering machine. When Gabriel was out of town, Paul was responsible for filing and selectively passing on these communications; he heard requests for help with surveying problems, demands for better speaking parts in *Hamlet*, instructions for the use of special effects such as lightning and small explosions. His position as a funnel for this stream of exotic visitors offset the combination of handicap and natural reticence which tended to let him slide into the careful circle of the blind.

Paul's studies in history required a lot of solitary reading, as did his work in the University Braille library. Outside of Gabriel's whirlwind of music and arguments, Paul's main solace was his collection of talking books. He would relax his cramped fingers, brew some herb tea and settle back in a cloud of fragrant steam to listen to *King Lear*, or a dramatic recital of *Beowulf* in Old English, or a commentary on Darwin's *The Origin of Species*, complete with recordings of bird calls. Shakespeare was Paul's favourite; he had versions of all the plays and sonnets. He had tried to explain his preference, and finally concluded that in Shakespeare, visual images were always more suggestive than descriptive: King Lear's storm of despair was only peripherally physical; Prospero's island and the forest of Arden were made up of selective associations, projections of worlds perceived in the mind. For Paul, visual images in literature were neither meaningless nor completely understandable: some triggered memory—sometimes sight, sometimes emotion; others did not. He found Shakespeare's symbolic landscapes especially comprehensive and real.

Paul's favourite sonnet was number 130, the one beginning:

> *My mistress' eyes are nothing like the sun;*
> *Coral is far more red than her lips' red: ...*

---

[1]**sitar:** a large stringed instrument originating in India

Paul's recording of this particular sonnet affected him to an extraordinary degree. Even more than the poetry, the voice of the reader, like music, seemed to enhance the significance of the words. It was a young woman's voice, slightly nasal but so clear and light as to be almost sexless; the self-conscious enunciation and mild distortion of the recording made it sound distant. Paul could imagine that he was hearing the woman for whom the sonnet had been written, reading it aloud for the first time, her voice blurred by centuries. The sonnet was part of a collection compiled by volunteer readers from the university; the reader of "Sonnet 130" was not named and did not appear on the rest of the recording. Paul had made several copies, as he was afraid of wearing out the original and being unable to replace it.

The sonnet had become so familiar that Paul found himself repeating it whenever he was slightly distracted, using it like a chant to measure distance when he was walking. Picking up his cane from the hall closet, he found his way down the stairs and out of the building. Turning left, he passed two lampposts:

> *If snow be white, why then her breasts are dun;*
> *If hairs be wires, black wires grow on her head.*

His relaxed mind offered him a brief view of snow-covered fields striped with a dark procession of pylons and connecting lines; the scene seemed to move past him before disappearing into his memory.

> *I have seen roses damasked, red and white,*
> *But no such roses see I in her cheeks;*

An imaginary smell of snow was replaced by the real, sweet scent coming from the flower stalls near the corner.

> *And in some perfumes is there more delight*
> *Than in the breath that from my mistress reeks.*

Paul felt the warm, malodorous rush of air coming up from the underground station and tapped his stick to find the first step down. He had memorized routes he could travel alone to get to the library and the university; today a friend was going to meet him at the link to the train station and travel with him to the conference.

Paul was no longer afraid of travelling by train, as repetition of the sightless experience had built up protective layers of routine. He now found it strangely exhilarating: the vibration, the press of people, the throbbing rattle of speed, all built and sustained an emotional tension and put Paul in a state of undefined expectation. He had discovered that train rides represented a way of reviving his memories. In addition to the dreams, train rides seemed to open up an unused store of associations, provoking vivid flashes of remembered sight. The effect sometimes lasted for several days. Paul had tried to explain the experience to Gabriel, who began referring to Paul's 'visions' as results of train 'trips.'

On the subway, Paul gripped the handle nearest the door, counting stops. He stepped out at the correct platform, inhaling the pervasive underground atmosphere of damp concrete and fighting the usual panic until he heard his friend's voice and felt a hand on his arm. As they headed for the ticket office, his apprehension suddenly produced the brilliant picture of a crowded station full of colour and movement. Some of the people Paul knew: he saw a ten-year-old friend who was now married, a neighbour with the dog he used to walk. Paul looked at other, strange faces and felt a mild unease. He climbed into his seat savouring the image; then he lost it as, with a starting jerk, the train began to move.

Paul returned from the conference feeling unhappy. Another student, a math major, had cornered Paul and forced him to discuss the different ways of presenting computerized geometry in Braille. Paul had lost interest in all but simple math when he had lost his sight. His pleasure in angles and lines had been purely visual; he could not understand the perspective of someone who had been blind from birth. As an added confusion, while the student was speaking, Paul involuntarily saw in perfect detail the figure of his father, twenty years earlier, as he had appeared trying to help Paul with his homework. As Paul watched helplessly, his father's image flickered and changed: his hair lengthened, then shortened as his skin darkened; his beard disappeared; a chequered shirt became striped, then was hidden under a sweater. Throughout these transformations, the young student's voice spoke as if from behind his father's face, which somehow managed to maintain an expression of earnest concern. Paul arrived back at the apartment with a sense of having lost something important, and by having it in the first place, had lost something else. For consolation he listened to ten of his favourite sonnets, ending with "Sonnet 130." Then he decided to go over the messages on the answering machine.

Gabriel had replaced the sitar with a sixteenth-century dulcimer;[2] a few delicate chords escaped before Paul pressed the correct button.

---

[2] **dulcimer:** a boxlike stringed instrument often played with mallets

A young woman's voice said clearly, "It's me." Paul was paralyzed; realizing he had missed the rest of the message, he rewound the tape. The slightly nasal intonation was unmistakable; Shakespeare's mistress was coming to collect her script at eight o'clock, as promised.

Her name was Emily Leonne; she was a forestry student who liked drama. She arrived still covered in pine needles from an afternoon field trip. When Paul let her in with a kind of horrified wonder, the scent of resin and damp earth streamed into the apartment. He thought he had opened the door to a forest. For a moment, he found himself looking into a stand of evergreens opposite that first platform, on that first day. A fox appeared at the edge of the tracks, loped neatly across and vanished into the trees.

Fantastically, the first word she spoke was his name. Gabriel must have told her. Her voice was gruffer, at once quicker and more hesitant than the recording.

> *I love to hear her speak, yet well I know*
> *That music hath a far more pleasing sound.*

When she agreed to go to a concert with him, Paul nearly drove Gabriel crazy with planning. He traced the route to the auditorium four times, counting blocks, turns, fire hydrants, streetlamps. Then he made himself sick worrying if she liked baroque music. Gabriel said if she didn't then what good was she anyway, and turned the radio up so that the bass thundered like a summer storm. Emily said she liked the concert and accepted a drink afterwards. After she left, Paul asked Gabriel what she looked like.

"Reddish hair; dark eyes—brown, I think."

Paul remembered the dark sleepers, the red flash of the fox.

> *I grant I never saw a goddess go:*
> *My mistress, when she walks, treads on the ground.*

He was silent, satisfied.

He asked her to another concert; in return, she brought him a pack of embossed cards and taught him to play poker with Gabriel. Paul gave her a necklace of agate, a cool, fluid weight of rounded stones; she arrived the next day with a balsam fir seedling from the nursery, carefully potted.

The first time Emily stayed the night, Paul remembered briefly as a revelation the red glow of closed eyelids. For the first time in years, he recognized the border between sleep and consciousness, then it faded into unimportance. He listened to Emily's heartbeat until it became a rhythm in a dream and he watched the shadows of trees passing, mile after mile, until the darkening sky made them indistinguishable.

Emily took Paul to the movies. They sat in the back and she whispered a blow-by-blow description of all the action she thought he was missing. These outings usually degenerated into normal back row foolishness when Emily began telling lies, giggling and commenting on their neighbours. As they walked out into the cold of the evening and on into the park (Emily still laughing), Paul felt as if the characters in the film with their choreographed ecstasy, and the other viewers with their cheerful passion, followed and surrounded them with the heady freshness of the new leaves.

She made him go to an evening of country dancing; she traced the patterns of each dance for him and taught him the steps. The other dancers whirled him around with congenial patronage. Paul could not decide whether he enjoyed himself or not; it was like being drunk. That night he dreamed of trying to keep his balance in a crowded corridor, jostled by faceless giants. He woke sweating, his heart beating quickly in time with the music.

Gabriel announced that as his current play was so successful he was going on tour. He left with a shout, his windbreaker rustling and snapping like the feathers of some huge bird. For a while it seemed to Paul that Gabriel still hovered in the apartment; half-eaten bags of cereal materialized from under cushions and the answering machine remained strongly vocal. Emily was much quieter than Gabriel, but no less detectable. Used to being untidy, she made an effort not to leave clothes on the floor where Paul might trip over them. As a result, all chairs and tables were carefully draped. Filmy scarves, work gloves, raincoats, all showed where Emily had just been, where she was going and where she was. Paul felt wonderfully secure, wrapped in this cocoon of reminders. Emily also filled the windowsills with small trees. For Paul, the apartment might have overlooked a vast wilderness; sun-warmed evergreen pervaded every room.

Emily read to him often. She agreed to tape other readings for him to keep, but only after some persuasion. Emily did not like her voice on recordings; she thought it sounded stilted, high-pitched, too childish. Paul had also noticed the difference between the live readings and the recordings. He loved Emily's voice and the possessive intimacy of listening to her, but he had come to realize that it was still the slightly distant, distorted voice that he found oddly compelling. Almost guiltily, he would take out his recordings and listen to them when she was away.

One day in the fall, Emily left early to catch the train for a foresters' clinic in the mountains. Paul got up late; he was still surprised by how much he noticed her absence. That evening, before she was due back —in a nostalgic, conspiratorial mood—he decided to listen to "Sonnet 130." He played the last lines through twice.

And yet, by heaven, I think my love as rare
As any she belied by false compare.

Paul reached over to open the window, spruce needles pricking his fingers. The wind that rushed in was cold; it was getting late. He sat back, breathing in the feral, resinous air, and felt vaguely anxious. The forest in his mind floated like a mirage on the other side of the tracks, silent and insubstantial.

When the telephone rang, Paul was so disoriented that it rang three times before he even reached the hall. He heard the answering machine click on and the throb of a drum mixed with the thick, green breath of the trees. Gabriel's voice announced his absence. The music paused, a note sounded and Paul heard Emily's voice, speaking against the noise of many other voices.

It seemed to Paul that he could still feel the resonance of the drum, but the tempo had become faster and steadier. His lungs filled with the cold of remembered snow. In his mind's eye he saw the fox, poised on the tracks. Fences began to writhe past him, stained pink by the dawn; trees shredded the sky around him; a flock of crows flew towards him at amazing speed. An ocean of white fields swelled up like a great tide and he saw the woman with the gun. For an instant, the skeleton of an abandoned barn framed the rising sun.

When Emily came in, a few minutes later, she was nearly knocked over as Paul grabbed at her and pressed his lips against her throat. He stumbled; his feet were tangled in long ribbons of tape and the remains of the stereo system. The answering machine lay sideways on the floor. There did not seem to be a way to tell her how, overwhelmed with visions, his heart pounding in time with the engine, he had suddenly seen his own face as he had last seen it, reflected in the train window. The telephone message sounded distant; the light voice spoke with nervous precision and sexless clarity. He heard the voice of this child, this eight-year-old self, distorted by the resonance of his own skull, saying:

"It won't be long. I'll be home soon." ❯

Hannah Grant has degrees from the University of St. Andrews, in Fife, Scotland, and the University of New Brunswick. Her short stories have been published in the journals *Voice, The Longmeadow Journal*, and *The Fiddlehead*. This story, "The Forest of Arden," was first published as the winner of the first Hemingway Prize offered in memory of Dan Hemingway, a student of the University of St. Andrews, and was later published in the collection *Coming Attractions '93*.

1. *Response*

a. Were there aspects of this story that you found difficult to understand? If so, explain what they were. What reading strategies helped you to deal with the story's complexities? Discuss your ideas in a group.

b. Explain the significance of the dream sequence with which the story opens.

c. In what way does the description in the second paragraph prepare the reader for the information about Paul's blindness? Why do you think the author withheld that information until the third paragraph?

d. How does the author integrate Shakespeare's "Sonnet CXXX" into the story? In a group, read the whole sonnet aloud, discuss its meaning, and comment on the functions it serves within the story.

e. What does Emily do to trigger Paul's final vision? What special significance does the vision hold for him?

2. *Literature Studies* Allusion

The title of this story is a literary **allusion** to a setting in one of Shakespeare's comedies. Using the Internet or other resources, identify which play the allusion refers to. If possible, find out whether Shakespeare's forest of Arden has a symbolic value that might contribute to the meaning of Grant's story. What other allusions does the story contain, and what do many of them have in common?

An **allusion** is a reference to another literary work, or a person, place, event, or object from history, literature, or mythology.

Things That Fly

by Douglas Coupland

I'm sitting hunched over the living room coffee table on a Sunday night, in a daze, having just woken up from a deep deep sleep on a couch shared with pizza boxes and crushed plastic cherry yogurt containers. In front of me a TV game show is playing on MUTE and my head rests on top of my hands, as though I am praying, but I am not; I am rubbing my eyes and trying to wake up, and my hair is brushing the tabletop which is covered in crumbs and I am thinking to myself that, in spite of everything that has happened in my life, I have never lost the sensation of always being on the brink of some magic revelation—that *if only* I would look closely enough at the world, then that magic revelation would be mine—*if only* I could wake up just that little bit more, then ... well—let me describe what happened today.

Today went like this: I was up at noon; instant coffee; watched a talk show; a game show; a bit of football; a religious something-or-other; then I turned the TV off. I drifted listlessly about the house, from silent room to silent room, spinning the wheels of the two mountain bikes on their racks in the hallway and straightening a pile of CDs glued together with spilled Orange Crush in the living room. I suppose I was trying to pretend I had real things to do, but, well, I didn't.

My brains felt overheated. So much has happened in my life recently. And after hours of this pointlessness I finally had to admit I couldn't take being alone one more moment. And so I swallowed my pride and drove to my parents at their house further up the hill here on the North Shore: up on the mountain— up in the trees to my old house—my true home, I guess. Today was the first day when I could really tell that summer was over. The cold air sparkled and the maple leaves were rotting, putting forth their lovely reek, like dead pancakes.

Up on the mountain, my mother was in the kitchen making 1947-style cream cheese sandwiches with pimentos and no crusts to freeze in advance for her bridge friends. Dad was sitting at the kitchen table reading *The Vancouver Sun*. Of course they knew about what had happened recently and so they were walking on eggshells around me. This made me feel odd and under-the-microscope, so I went upstairs to sit in the guest room to look out the window at honking V's of Canada geese flying south toward the United States from northern British Columbia. It was peaceful to see so many birds flying—to see all these things in our world that can fly.

Mom had left the TV on in the bedroom, next room over. CNN was saying that Superman was scheduled to die later this week—in the sky above Minneapolis, and I was momentarily taken out of myself. I thought this was certainly a coincidence, because I had just visited the city of Minneapolis a month ago, on a business trip: a new crystal city, all shiny like quartz rising over the Midwest corn fields. According to the TV, Superman was supposed to die in an air battle over the city with a supremely evil force, and while I knew this was just a cheesy publicity ploy to sell more comics—and I haven't even *read* a Superman comic in two decades— the thought still made me feel bad.

And then the geese passed, and I sat watching the blue smoke linger down the mountain slopes from people burning leaves across the Capilano River. After a while I returned downstairs and Dad and I sat in the kitchen next to the sliding glass door and we fed the birds and animals on the back patio. We had grain and corn for the chickadees, juncos and starlings; and roasted peanuts for the jays and the black and grey squirrels. Such a sea of life! And I was glad for this activity because there is something about the animals that takes us out of ourselves and takes us out of time and allows us to forget our own lives.

Dad had placed a cob of corn on a stump for the jays, who bickered over it non-stop. And we threw peanuts to the jays and I noticed that when I threw two peanuts to a jay, it just sat there and couldn't decide which nut was juicier, so it became paralyzed with greed and couldn't take either of them. And we threw nuts to the squirrels, too, and they're so dumb that even if I hit them on the head with a nut, they couldn't find it. I just don't know how they've managed to survive these millions of years. Dad had also scattered sunflower seeds for a flying squirrel he has named Yo-yo who lives in the backyard. Yo-yo darted about the yard like a pinball.

Mom said that people are interested in birds only inasmuch as they exhibit human behavior—greed and stupidity and anger—and by doing so they free us from the unique sorrow of being human. She thinks humans are tired of having to take the blame all by themselves for the badness in the world.

I told Mom my own theory of why we like birds—of how birds are a miracle because they prove to us there is a finer, simpler state of being which we may strive to attain.

A good writer turns fact into truth.

Edward Albee

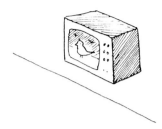

But anyway, I began feeling low again, and I felt I was making Mom and Dad feel uncomfortable because they were worrying I might go to pieces at any moment. I could see the relief on their faces when I laughed at the jays, like I'd been cured, and this depressed me, made me feel like a freak, and so I went back upstairs, into the TV room, turned on the TV and hid. I got to thinking about all of the bad stuff that had happened in life recently. It made me think of all of the bad things I had done to other people in my world—and there have been so many bad things I have done. I felt ashamed; I was feeling as though none of the good deeds I had ever done had ever mattered.

And on the TV there were still more birds! Such lovely creatures and I thought that we are so lucky to have the animals. What act of goodness did we as humans once commit to deserve such kindness from God?

There was a pretty grey parakeet who had learned to recognize human things—triangle shapes and car keys and the color blue—and to speak the words for them. This little parakeet worked so hard to remember these things, and it had an efficient faraway female voice like a telephone operator in Texas. The parakeet made me realize how hard it is to learn anything in life, and even then, there's no guarantee you might need it.

On another channel there were pictures of a zoo in Miami, Florida, which had been whacked by a hurricane and there were pictures of ducks and tall elegant birds swimming in the wreckage except they didn't know it was wreckage. It was just the world.

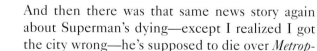

And then there was that same news story again about Superman's dying—except I realized I got the city wrong—he's supposed to die over *Metropolis*, not Minneapolis. But I was still sad. I have always liked the idea of Superman because I have always liked the idea that there is one person in the world who doesn't do bad things. And that there is one person in the world who is able to fly.

I myself often have dreams in which I am flying, but it's not flying the way Superman does. I simply put my arms behind my shoulders and float and move. Needless to say, it is my favorite dream.

Back on TV there were pictures of whooping cranes doing a mating dance and they were so sweet and graceful and I thought, "If only *I* could be a whooping crane and was able to float and fly like them, then it would be like always being in love."

And then I got just plain lonely and just so fed up with all the badness in my life and in the world and I said to myself, "Please, God, just make me a bird— that's all I ever really wanted—a white graceful bird free of shame and taint and fear of loneliness, and give me other white birds among which to fly, and give me a sky so big and wide that if I never wanted to land, I would never have to."

But instead God gave me these words, and I speak them here.

And I will add in closing that when I got back home tonight, I stepped through the door and over my messes; I fell onto the couch and into a sleep and then into a dream, and I dreamed that I was back in Minneapolis, back next to the corn fields. I dreamed I had taken a glass elevator to the top of one of the city's green glass sky-scrapers, to the very top floor, and I was running around that floor from one face of the skyscraper to another, frantic, looking through those big sheets of glass—trying to find a way to protect Superman. ❱

Douglas Coupland was born in 1961 on a Canadian military base in Germany. When he was four, he returned to Canada with his family. In 1984, he graduated from the Emily Carr College of Art and Design in Vancouver. After graduation, he studied abroad, eventually completing a two-year program in Japanese business science at a school in Japan. Although Coupland first became an artist, he is more famous for his writing. Of his nine novels to date, *Generation X, Life After God,* and *Lara's Book: Lara Croft and the Tomb Raider Phenomenon* are his most popular.

1. *Response*
    a. Make a list of the factual information the story provides about the narrator. Based on this list, what would you say about the amount and type of factual information the reader learns about the narrator?
    b. Reading between the lines, what do you think might have happened to the narrator in the recent past? What clues helped you reach those conclusions?
    c. The narrator tells this story as an extended flashback. Explain why you think this narrative technique is or is not appropriate to the story.
    d. Reread the story carefully. Do you see any signs that the narrator has found a possible remedy for his despair? Support your opinion with evidence from the text.

2. *Literature Studies* *Symbolism* The story contains several references to birds and to the comic-book character Superman. Reread the story carefully and suggest how these "things that fly" function as symbols. Do the symbols have more than one meaning? Explain how the symbols help to develop the meaning of the story.

3. **Language Conventions** *Conversational Tone* "Things That Fly" is written in a conversational tone. Find specific examples of techniques Coupland uses to create that feeling. Consider details such as sentence structure, punctuation, diction, and so on. Suggest some reasons why Coupland might have preferred a conversational tone. Do you think that the tone is effective? Why or why not?

4. **Visual Communication** *Line Drawings* Coupland's line drawings add an unusual visual element to this short story. In your view, do these illustrations add to or detract from the story? Explain.

   Write a brief story of your own (two or three pages) that contains a visual component—line drawings, colour illustrations, or special fonts, for example. Present your story to a group and explain what you were trying to accomplish with your visuals.

Once the disease of reading has laid hold upon
the system it weakens it so that it falls easy prey
to that other scourge which dwells in the inkpot and
festers in the quill. The wretch takes to writing.
—Virginia Woolf

Theme Connections

- "Groom Service," a story about a young man who despairs of winning over the woman he loves, Vol. I, p. 12
- "Transients in Arcadia," a story about a couple dissatisfied with their normal lives, Vol. I, p. 37
- "The Return," a story in which one character faces despair and loneliness, Vol. I, p. 44
- "Loneliness," a poem about loneliness, Vol. I, p. 244
- "That's Extraordinary!" a radio play about a lonely woman, Vol. II, p. 179

Could the fate of the world ultimately depend on the swing of a golf club?

The Large Ant

by Howard Fast

There have been all kinds of notions and guesses as to how it would end. One held that sooner or later there would be too many people; another that we would do each other in, and the atom bomb made that a very good likelihood. All sorts of notions, except the simple fact that we were what we were. We could find a way to feed any number of people and perhaps even a way to avoid wiping each other out with the bomb; those things we are very good at, but we have never been any good at changing ourselves or the way we behave.

I know. I am not a bad man or a cruel man; quite to the contrary, I am an ordinary, humane person, and I love my wife and my children and I get along with my neighbors. I am like a great many other men, and do the things they would do and just as thoughtlessly. There it is in a nutshell.

I am also a writer, and I told Lieberman, the curator, and Fitzgerald, the government man, that I would like to write down the story. They shrugged their shoulders. "Go ahead," they said, "because it won't make one bit of difference."

"You don't think it would alarm people?"

"How can it alarm anyone when nobody will believe it?"

"If I could have a photograph or two."

"Oh, no," they said then. "No photographs."

"What kind of sense does that make?" I asked them. "You are willing to let me write the story—why not the photographs so that people could believe me?"

"They still won't believe you. They will just say you faked the photographs, but no one will believe you. It will make for more confusion, and if we have a chance of getting out of this, confusion won't help."

"What will help?"

They weren't ready to say that, because they didn't know. So here is what happened to me, in a very straightforward and ordinary manner.

Every summer, some time in August, four good friends of mine and I go for a week's fishing on the St. Regis chain of lakes in the Adirondacks. We rent the same shack each summer; we drift around in canoes and sometimes we catch a few bass. The fishing isn't very good, but we play cards well together, and we cook out and generally relax. This summer past, I had some things to do that couldn't be put off. I arrived three days late, and the weather was so warm and even and beguiling that I decided to stay on by myself for a day or two after the others left. There was a small flat lawn in front of the shack, and I made up my mind to spend at least three or four hours at short putts. That was how I happened to have the putting iron next to my bed.

The first day I was alone, I opened a can of beans and a can of beer for my supper. Then I lay down in my bed with *Life on the Mississippi*,[1] a pack of cigarettes and an eight-ounce chocolate bar. There was nothing I had to do, no telephone, no demands and no newspapers. At that moment, I was about as contented as any man can be in these nervous times.

It was still light outside, and enough light came in through the window above my head for me to read by. I was just reaching for a fresh cigarette, when I looked up and saw it on the foot of my bed. The edge of my hand was touching the golf club, and with a single motion I swept the club over and down, struck it a savage and accurate blow and killed it. That was what I referred to before. Whatever kind of a man I am, I react as a man does. I think that any man, black, white or yellow, in China, Africa or Russia, would have done the same thing.

First I found that I was sweating all over, and then I knew I was going to be sick. I went outside to vomit, recalling that this hadn't happened to me since 1943, on my way to Europe on a tub of a Liberty ship. Then I felt better and was able to go back into the shack and look at it. It was quite dead, but I had already made up my mind that I was not going to sleep alone in this shack.

---

[1] **Life on the Mississippi:** Samuel Clemens' (Mark Twain) memoir of his time as a steamboat pilot, published in 1875

I couldn't bear to touch it with my bare hands. With a piece of brown paper, I picked it up and dropped it into my fishing creel. That, I put into the trunk of my car, along with what luggage I carried. Then I closed the door of the shack, got into my car and drove back to New York. I stopped once along the road, just before I reached the Thruway, to nap in the car for a little over an hour. It was almost dawn when I reached the city, and I had shaved, had a hot bath and changed my clothes before my wife awoke.

During breakfast, I explained that I was never much of a hand at the solitary business, and since she knew that, and since driving alone all night was by no means an extraordinary procedure for me, she didn't press me with any questions. I had two eggs, coffee and a cigarette. Then I went into my study, lit another cigarette, and contemplated my fishing creel, which sat upon my desk.

My wife looked in, saw the creel, remarked that it had too ripe a smell, and asked me to remove it to the basement.

"I'm going to dress," she said. The kids were still at camp. "I have a date with Ann for lunch—I had no idea you were coming back. Shall I break it?"

"No, please don't. I can find things to do that have to be done."

Then I sat and smoked some more, and finally I called the Museum, and asked who the curator of insects was. They told me his name was Bertram Lieberman, and I asked to talk to him. He had a pleasant voice. I told him that my name was Morgan, and that I was a writer, and he politely indicated that he had seen my name and read something that I had written. That is formal procedure when a writer introduces himself to a thoughtful person.

I asked Lieberman if I could see him, and he said that he had a busy morning ahead of him. Could it be tomorrow?

"I am afraid it has to be now," I said firmly.

"Oh? Some information you require."

"No. I have a specimen for you."

"Oh?" The "oh" was a cultivated, neutral interval. It asked and answered and said nothing. You have to teach at least five semesters at a college to develop that particular "oh."

"Yes. I think you will be interested."

"An insect?" he asked mildly.

"I think so."

"Oh? Large?"

"Quite large," I told him.

"Eleven o'clock? Can you be here then? On the main floor, to the right, as you enter."

"I'll be there," I said.

"One thing—dead?"

"Yes, it's dead."

"Oh?" again. "I'll be happy to see you at eleven o'clock, Mr. Morgan."

My wife was dressed now. She opened the door to my study and said firmly, "Do get rid of that fishing creel. It smells."

"Yes, darling. I'll get rid of it."

"I should think you'd want to take a nap after driving all night."

"Funny, but I'm not sleepy," I said. "I think I'll drop around to the Museum."

My wife said that was what she liked about me, that I never tired of places like museums, police courts and third-rate night clubs.

Anyway, aside from a racetrack, a museum is the most interesting and unexpected place in the world. It was unexpected to have two other men waiting for me, along with Mr. Lieberman, in his office. Lieberman was a skinny, sharp-faced man of about sixty. The government man, Fitzgerald, was small, dark-eyed and wore gold-rimmed glasses. He was very alert, but he never told me what part of the government he represented. He just said "we," and it meant the government. Hopper, the third man, was comfortable-looking, pudgy, and genial. He was a United States senator with an interest in entomology, although before this morning I would have taken better than even money that such a thing not only wasn't, but could not be.

The room was large and square and plainly furnished, with shelves and cupboards on all walls.

We shook hands, and then Lieberman asked me, nodding at the creel, "Is that it?"

"That's it."

"May I?"

"Go ahead," I told him. "It's nothing that I want to stuff for the parlor. I'm making you a gift of it."

"Thank you, Mr. Morgan," he said, and then he opened the creel and looked inside. Then he straightened up, and the two other men looked at him inquiringly.

He nodded. "Yes."

The senator closed his eyes for a long moment. Fitzgerald took off his glasses and wiped them industriously. Lieberman spread a piece of plastic on his desk, and then lifted the thing out of my creel and laid it on the plastic. The two men didn't move. They just sat where they were and looked at it.

"What do you think it is, Mr. Morgan?" Lieberman asked me.

"I thought that was your department."

"Yes, of course. I only wanted your impression."

"An ant. That's my impression. It's the first time I saw an ant fourteen, fifteen inches long. I hope it's the last."

"An understandable wish," Lieberman nodded.

Fitzgerald said to me, "May I ask how you killed it, Mr. Morgan?"

"With an iron. A golf club, I mean. I was doing a little fishing with some friends up at St. Regis in the Adirondacks, and I brought the iron for my short shots. They're the worst part of my game, and when my friends left, I intended to stay on at our shack and do four or five hours of short putts. You see—"

"There's no need to explain," Hopper smiled, a trace of sadness on his face. "Some of our very best golfers have the same trouble."

"I was lying in bed, reading, and I saw it at the foot of my bed. I had the club—"

"I understand," Fitzgerald nodded.

"You avoid looking at it," Hopper said.

"It turns my stomach."

"Yes—yes, I suppose so."

Lieberman said, "Would you mind telling us why you killed it, Mr. Morgan?"

"Why?"

"Yes—why?"

"I don't understand you," I said. "I don't know what you're driving at."

"Sit down, please, Mr. Morgan," Hopper nodded. "Try to relax. I'm sure this has been very trying."

"I still haven't slept. I want a chance to dream before I say how trying."

"We are not trying to upset you, Mr. Morgan," Lieberman said. "We do feel, however, that certain aspects of this are very important. That is why I am asking you why you killed it. You must have had a reason. Did it seem about to attack you?"

"No."

"Or make any sudden motion toward you?"

"No. It was just there."

"Then why?"

"This is to no purpose," Fitzgerald put in. "We know why he killed it."

"Do you?" I nodded. "You're clearer on the subject than I am."

"The answer is very simple, Mr. Morgan. You killed it because you are a human being."

"Oh?" I borrowed that from Lieberman.

"Yes. Do you understand?"

"No, I don't."

"Then why did you kill it?" Hopper put in.

"I saw it," I answered slowly, "and somehow I knew that I must kill it. I didn't think or decide. I just grabbed the iron and hit it."

"Precisely," Fitzgerald said.

"You were afraid?" Hopper asked.

"I was scared to death. I still am, to tell the truth."

Lieberman said, "You are an intelligent man, Mr. Morgan. Let me show you something." He then opened the doors to one of the wall cupboards, and there stood eight jars of formaldehyde and in each jar a specimen like mine—and in each case mutilated by the violence of its death. I said nothing. I just stared.

Lieberman closed the cupboard doors. "All in five days," he shrugged.

"A new race of ants," I whispered stupidly.

"No. They're not ants. Come here!" He motioned me to the desk and the other two joined me. Lieberman took a set of dissection instruments out of his drawer, used one to turn the thing over, and then pointed to the underpart of what would be the thorax in an insect.

"That looks like part of him, doesn't it, Mr. Morgan?"

"Yes, it does."

Using two of the tools, he found a fissure and pried the bottom apart. It came open like the belly of a bomber; it was a pocket, a pouch, a receptacle that the thing wore, and in it were four beautiful little tools or instruments or weapons, each about an inch and a half long. They were beautiful the way any object of functional purpose and loving creation is beautiful—the way the creature itself would have been beautiful, had it not been an insect and myself a man. Using tweezers, Lieberman took each instrument out of the brackets that held it, offering each to me. And I took each one, felt it, examined it, and then put it down.

I had to look at the ant now, and I realized that I had not truly looked at it before. We don't look carefully at a thing that is horrible or repugnant to us. You can't look carefully at a thing through a screen of hatred. But now the hatred and the fear were diluted, and as I looked, I realized it was not an ant although like an ant. It was nothing that I had ever seen or dreamed of.

All three men were watching me, and suddenly I was on the defensive. "I didn't know! What do you expect when you see an insect that size?"

The Large Ant • **155**

Lieberman nodded.

"What in the name of God is it?"

From his desk, Lieberman produced a bottle and four small glasses. He poured it and we drank it neat. I would not have expected him to keep good Scotch in his desk.

"We don't know," Hopper said. "We don't know what it is."

Lieberman pointed to the broken skull, from which a white substance oozed. "Brain material—a great deal of it."

"It could be a very intelligent creature," Hopper nodded.

Lieberman said, "It is an insect in developmental structure. We know very little about intelligence in our insects. It's not the same as what we call intelligence. It's a collective phenomenon—as if you were to think of the component parts of our bodies. Each part is alive, but the intelligence is a result of the whole. If that same pattern were to extend to creatures like this one—"

I broke the silence. They were content to stand there and stare at it.

"Suppose it were?"

"What?"

"The kind of collective intelligence you were talking about."

"Oh? Well, I couldn't say. It would be something beyond our wildest dreams. To us—well, what we are to an ordinary ant."

"I don't believe that," I said shortly, and Fitzgerald, the government man, told me quietly, "Neither do we. We guess. We comfort ourselves, too."

"If it's that intelligent, why didn't it use one of those weapons on me?"

"Would that be a mark of intelligence?" Hopper asked mildly.

"Perhaps none of these is a weapon," Lieberman said.

"Don't you know? Didn't the others carry instruments?"

"They did," Fitzgerald said shortly.

"Why? What were they?"

"We don't know," Lieberman said.

"But you can find out. We have scientists, engineers—good God, this is an age of fantastic instruments. Have them taken apart!"

"We have."

"Then what have you found out?"

"Nothing."

"Do you mean to tell me," I said, "that you can find out nothing about these instruments—what they are, how they work, what their purpose is?"

"Exactly," Hopper nodded. "Nothing, Mr. Morgan. They are meaningless to the finest engineers and technicians in the United States. You know the old story—suppose you gave a radio to Aristotle? What would he do with it? Where would he find power? And what would he receive with no one to send? It is not that these instruments are complex. They are actually very simple. We simply have no idea of what they can or should do."

"But there must be a weapon of some kind."

"Why?" Lieberman demanded. "Look at yourself, Mr. Morgan—a cultured and intelligent man, yet you cannot conceive of a mentality that does not include weapons as a prime necessity. Yet a weapon is an unusual thing, Mr. Morgan. An instrument of murder. We don't think that way, because the weapon has become the symbol of the world we inhabit. Is that civilized, Mr. Morgan? Or are the weapon and civilization in the ultimate sense incompatible? Can you imagine a mentality to which the concept of murder is impossible—or let me say absent. We see everything through our own subjectivity. Why shouldn't some other—this creature, for example—see the process of mentation[2] out of his subjectivity. So he approaches a creature of our world—and he is slain. Why? What explanation? Tell me, Mr. Morgan, what conceivable explanation could we offer a wholly rational creature for this," pointing to the thing on his desk. "I am asking you the question most seriously. What explanation?"

"An accident?" I muttered.

"And the eight jars in my cupboard? Eight accidents?"

"I think, Dr. Lieberman," Fitzgerald said, "that you can go a little too far in that direction."

"Yes, you would think so. It's a part of your own background. Mine is as a scientist. As a scientist, I try to be rational when I can. The creation of a structure of good and evil, or what we call morality and ethics, is a function of intelligence—and unquestionably the ultimate evil may be the destruction of conscious intelligence. That is why, so long ago, we at least recognized the injunction, 'Thou shalt not kill!' even if we never gave more than lip service to it. But to a collective intelligence, such as that of which this might be a part, the concept of murder would be monstrous beyond the power of thought."

I sat down and lit a cigarette. My hands were trembling. Hopper apologized. "We have been rather rough with you, Mr. Morgan. But over the past days, eight other people have done just what you did. We are caught in the trap of being what we are."

"But tell me—where do these things come from?"

---

[2]**mentation:** thinking

"It almost doesn't matter where they come from," Hopper said hopelessly. "Perhaps from another planet—perhaps from inside this one—or the moon or Mars. That doesn't matter. Fitzgerald thinks they come from a smaller planet, because their movements are apparently slow on earth. But Dr. Lieberman thinks that they move slowly because they have not discovered the need to move quickly. Meanwhile, they have the problem of murder and what to do with it. Heaven knows how many of them have died in other places—Africa, Asia, Europe."

"Then why don't you publicize this? Put a stop to it before it's too late!"

"We've thought of that," Fitzgerald nodded. "What then—panic, hysteria, charges that this is the result of the atom bomb? We can't change. We are what we are."

"They may go away," I said.

"Yes, they may," Lieberman nodded. "But if they are without the curse of murder, they may also be without the curse of fear. They may be social in the highest sense. What does society do with a murderer?"

"There are societies that put him to death—and there are other societies that recognize his sickness and lock him away, where he can kill no more," Hopper said. "Of course, when a whole world is on trial, that's another matter. We have atom bombs now and other things, and we are reaching out to the stars—"

"I'm inclined to think that they'll run," Fitzgerald put in. "They may just have that curse of fear, Doctor."

"They may," Lieberman admitted. "I hope so."

But the more I think so, the more it seems to me that fear and hatred are the two sides of the same coin. I keep trying to think back, to recreate the moment when I saw it standing at the foot of my bed in the fishing shack. I keep trying to drag out of my memory a clear picture of what it looked like, whether behind that chitinous face and the two gently waving antennae there was any evidence of fear and anger. But the clearer the memory becomes, the more I seem to recall a certain wonderful dignity and repose. Not fear and not anger.

And more and more, as I go about my work, I get the feeling of what Hopper called "a world on trial." I have no sense of anger myself. Like a criminal who can no longer live with himself, I am content to be judged.

Howard Fast was born in 1914 in New York City. A high school drop-out, he published his first novel, *Two Valleys*, before his twentieth birthday and his most recent novel, *Greenwich*, in 2000. He is best known for his novels *Spartacus*, *Citizen Tom Paine*, and *The Last Frontier*. Along with his writing, Fast is known for his controversial membership in the Communist Party and for being awarded the Stalin Peace Prize.

1. *Response*
   a. What techniques does the author use to make an improbable situation seem believable? In your opinion, was he successful? Explain.
   b. In your opinion, is characterization an important element of this story? Why or why not?
   c. In your own words, summarize the philosophical perspective Howard Fast presents in "The Large Ant." What do you think his purpose was in writing the story, and why did he choose the science fiction genre to express his message?
   d. The characters in "The Large Ant" seem paralyzed by their dilemma. What course of action would *you* recommend to them?

2. *Critical Thinking* According to Fitzgerald, the government man, "'We can't change. We are what we are.'" Is humanity innately violent, and are we truly incapable of changing that? Discuss these issues in a small group.

3. *Focus on Context* Search for specific references, details, and behaviour in the story that imply that it took place many years ago. Make a list of the evidence you find and explain how it helps a reader identify the story's context. What reading and viewing skills do you rely on to help you identify the historical context for a particular literary or media work?

4. *Film Study* With a small group, brainstorm the titles for movies about encounters between humans and intelligent life from other planets. In these movies, what are some of the common human responses to alien life? Assess whether most of the movies support or refute Fast's message in "The Large Ant."

He was swimming for his life …

A Drowning

by Mark Ferguson

I watched him drown. The boat was far too close to the shore. There was engine trouble. I could see him working furiously trying to get it started. The seas were huge and the punt drifted in. All at once one swell broke, all round him, she went over, and I saw him leaping and thrown clear. Next I saw him there shocked in the water, but swimming evenly, fighting it, swimming away from the rocks, staying on top of the water, the white foam all over his darkly clad form like an otter in a brook. The next swell picked him up and swept in onto the low cliffs, onto the big black splintered rocks at their feet. Down he went a first time. I thought, I won't see him no more, but I was wrong. He came up a few yards shy of shore. I was shouting then. He was swimming mad out of there, swimming for his life, and another swell rolling in. It broke early, running down onto him like an avalanche for eighty or a hundred feet, a white wall tumbling and rushing forward to drown him. I saw him watching it come, paddling calmly out toward it and then I saw him duck under just as it struck where he had been. Smart, I was thinking, smart, but he was gone under a second time. I waited. The sea rose and boiled then sank away and back. The punt was already smashed, caught high up in the teeth of the land with tons and tons of water pouring back into the sea, off of the rocks and cliffs. The splintered wood of planks and torn brown strands of kelp in the blue-green.

He burst from below a second time, like a shot, his arm first, punching into air, swimming before he was even back on top of the water, swimming out to sea.

A third swell came then, larger than the others. I saw him see it. I saw him stop thrashing forward. I saw him turn sideways in the water, and look to the land, sizing up his chance. On it came. My arms jerked up—like a spasm and involuntary, waving for no reason really, a human impulse, a need to be recognized, to identify to him that I was there, even in the extraordinary circumstances. At all costs, waving only for him to notice me, to know that I was a witness. I did not speak, was not shouting, only my one big wave of both arms up over the head once. I left them up there, nothing but the helpless arms. I saw him then seeing me. He stared at me for one moment, held me in his eye, and there was no reproach, and no terror then, but something. Resignation maybe, like a tiredness, him knowing for an instant that I was something, a part of something back on land that he was really an incredibly long way off from. Never would he know it again. He was into something altogether different now. The connection between him and me, between his living breathing self and me, was pulled so thin and so taut in that moment, almost non-existent, not much longer now. No noise from him in the rueful moment, or maybe it was buried in the crashing seas and the jeering wind. And no noise from me, or maybe was I calling? And the speed was funny, the thing happening so slowly.

He went back to what he had been doing, what was really occupying him fully by then. He'd watch the third sea and then he'd watch the land, the sea, the land, and the sea seemed almost insane to me. Incredibly enough it seemed to keep on mounting, to keep growing, getting huge, getting heavy and dark—I know waves always do that when they come to the land—but this one time, this wave seemed ridiculous and wrong; it was breaking rules, the laws of waves or the rules had changed for that moment, and the fact that waves should rise up and break themselves onto the land seemed just then completely wrong, nothing only ugly and stupid. He looked so calm floating in the water, beautiful. As the beginning of the swell reached him, rising, I saw him treading calmly, now facing the land, his eyes fixed steadily on it. He must have chosen a spot he thought that he might just make, where he might just climb out of the wave and step magically back onto the land, soaked but safe. His whole thinking right then was determined by the concentration on that one wild hope. Then up he rose, and up he rose with the terrible sea. It rushed, it positively rushed on in then, gaining speed as it fell, and he had the whole crest to himself, that's how he rode in.

The world becomes utterly mute then, no sound, nothing, and I am the deafest one of them all, so utterly deaf it brings tears to my seeing eyes. That is how totally silent I remember it being. I see his face, his mouth open in a shout, half shock or surprise, half terror, his arms out meeting the crazy canted walls of rock, disappearing. I wonder can he still see his spot, can he still see that place he will land himself, step out of the sea? For how long does he think it will happen, for how long does he hold out, hold on to that one thought? Is it to the very last?

He was gone under for the third time, he disappeared completely then. He was out of sight and I never saw him then and he didn't come back up. How quiet was it? That total silence still when I turned away after a long time and he still hadn't resurfaced. I glanced back a few times, slowly climbing and clinging to the scrape and still no sign and a few times when I looked I thought, There. But when I looked a while it would just be a piece of wood or a this or a that. It stayed quiet like that for ages all the way back, and even when I got back, their voices at first were barely audible. They were talking but their voices were all really flat-sounding and seemed a long way off.

First person I met was John Mortimer waving from down a small pasture, feeding a horse out of a brin bag.[1] He shouts and I barely make him out. "Beautiful," he says, "Beautiful day." "Yes," I say. Because it was—it was still sunny and very breezy and dry and not too hot and it felt like it'd keep on like that another day or two for sure. All the women had their laundry and their fish out. I went home, told Dad and I stayed in the kitchen there with Mom and she got me some bread and jam and some tea and he went on to tell everyone else, to go and get a boat, try and find his body. The little cat had got in again, walking around the kitchen, meowing for supper. We ignored her for a long time till Mom said something offhand to her, and we had a little laugh, not paying attention then, and then Mrs. Abbott came in looking really very sad.

---

[1] **brin bag:** a sack made of burlap

Mark Ferguson lives in St. John's, Newfoundland and Labrador, and has been a member of The Burning Rock, a writer's collective, for a number of years. He is a short fiction writer whose work often has a St. John's or Placentia Bay setting.

I. *Response*
    a. What is the impact of the opening line of the story?
    b. What inferences about the narrator did you draw based on the information you were given? Compare your answers with those of a few other classmates. Why do you think the author gives so few details about the story's main characters?
    c. What does the conclusion of the story suggest about the community in which the story takes place?
    d. "A Drowning" explores one of the so-called "big questions": the question of mortality. In your journal or notebook, write a personal response to "A Drowning" and the message it conveys.

2. *Literature Studies* *Plot* Would you agree with the suggestion that the climax of "A Drowning" seems to occur at the very beginning of the story? To answer the question, analyse the story's plot structure using a plot diagram. Compare your diagram with a partner's; did you reach the same conclusions? Once you have considered the plot as a whole, discuss whether Ferguson starts his story effectively. Be prepared to explain your ideas.

3. *Making Connections* Use the Internet or other library resources to find the poem "Musée des Beaux Arts" by W. H. Auden and the painting "Fall of Icarus" by Pieter Breughel. What do these two works have in common with "A Drowning"? Present your ideas in the form of a brief written or oral report.

4. *Language Conventions* *Verb Tense* At a decisive moment in the story, Ferguson switches the verb tense he is using. Identify where this occurs, explain how the verb tense changes, and create a convincing explanation for why the author might have used this technique. Does Ferguson continue with the new tense until the end of the story? Why or why not? Present your own opinion about the effectiveness of Ferguson's use of verb tense.

"I take my mother's hand in mine. Her hands are bony and crooked, her fingers rough and hard like wood."

Red Bean Ice

by Nancy Lee

I dress my daughter in a warm coat. November air has an angry bite. As I slip her knapsack onto her shoulders, we argue about a hat and scarf. I tell her to wear them; she says they are too itchy. We settle on the scarf. We are getting ready to visit my mother at the Chinese Centre. I call it the Centre because I cannot bear to call it the Home as everyone else does.

Two months ago, on a Saturday afternoon, my mother's stay in our home ended when a policeman presented her and my daughter at our front door. He had found them wandering around Chinatown; my mother, disoriented; my five-year-old, crying. The pockets of my daughter's coat were filled with candy. Her shoes were missing. I questioned my mother as to the whereabouts of the shoes. She shook her head and broke into an awkward smile. "What shoes?"

That night my husband and I fought. He had visited a care facility for my mother. I was furious that he had done so behind my back. He was pleased with himself: the green-eyed, blonde Canadian had found a good home for his Chinese mother-in-law. He had a colour brochure. They had medical staff; they spoke her language.

"I speak her language!" I shouted.

"She'll be with people her own age," he reasoned. "Maybe she already knows some of them."

"Just because we all look alike doesn't mean we know each other."

My daughter is straggling behind. I turn around and hold out my gloved hand.

"Come on."

She takes my hand but forces her weight onto it to slow us both down. "It's raining."

"I know it's raining. I told you to wear the hat." I pull my daughter along. Her feet stumble with reluctance.

"Why can't we go in the car?" Her knapsack has slipped down her arms, dangles in the crook of her elbow. She is hoping I will offer to carry it.

I resist the urge to baby her. "Because we're taking the bus."

"But why?" She swings her arm; the knapsack jerks and snaps between us.

"Because, it's fun."

It is a rainy Saturday morning. I am seven years old. My mother and I ride the number twenty-two bus to Chinatown.

My mother speaks to me quietly; her melodic Cantonese floats lightly between us. She does not look at me and I do not look at her. Instead, we watch the scenery drift by. Her counsel, an immigrant voice-over for the moving city at the window.

Kensington Community Centre. "Homework is very important. Smart girls study hard. Education is the most important thing."

The curve in the road as it changes from Knight Street to Clark Drive just before 12th Avenue. "You must be a good person in your heart. Even when bad things happen."

The turn onto Venables Street, where a bed warehouse is advertised by a dancing mattress with hands and feet. "Sometimes it is good to laugh, not be so serious about things."

The sharp right turn into Chinatown, the street signs in both English and Chinese. "It is very important to respect your elders. Be a good person." My mother whispers this last sentiment as if it is a secret not to be shared with the rest of the bus.

The first few houses at the entrance to Chinatown are frighteningly old and filthy. Most of them have porches on the verge of collapse and make-shift curtains torn from flags or bed sheets. Layers of paint peel, wooden boards hang, and on the porch sit battered pieces of indoor furniture; a rotting recliner, a festering love seat. My mother shakes her head and clicks her tongue in disgust. It shames her that the Chinese district is an area rimmed with drunks and vagrants.

After the houses, come the shops which stretch from one end of Chinatown to the other; grocery stores with dry goods piled onto their shelves and cardboard boxes of fresh produce spilling onto the sidewalk. I pull the string to ring the bell and my mother and I get off the bus.

We hold hands as we walk past the loud grocers. A Chinese man with a knife stands on the sidewalk and yells at my mother as we pass by. "Oranges on special today! Very sweet!" He offers my mother a single slice of orange on a large sharp blade. My mother nods; the fruit is sweet. My mother sifts through the oranges in the cardboard box.

"That one is sweet, but what about these?"

The man chuckles and cuts her a fresh orange from the box. My mother hands the slice to me.

"Sweet?"

I nod and chew the slice while my mother stuffs oranges into a plastic bag.

At the fish mongers, I watch lobsters and crabs in the giant tanks. Claws snapping, bodies climbing in slow motion. The old and damaged trapped in the bottom corners of the tank. My mother pokes the slimy silver bodies laid out on mounds of crushed ice. "Very fresh! Very fresh!" the man in the white coat shouts as he waves his knife at my mother.

"Too many bones," my mother says tersely. The man scans the fish, as if with x-ray vision, searches for one with fewer bones. Then he nods dramatically and pulls one from the pile, holds it up for my mother's inspection. My mother stares at the fish, and like the man, uses her magic Chinese sight to count the bones. She nods and tells him to leave the head on.

At the meat market, flattened ducks twirl in the window, Chinese sausages hang like thick beaded curtains. The smell is sweet, like soya sauce and honey.

"A pound of barbecued pork," my mother orders. The man with the cleaver reaches for a piece of meat, but my mother stops him. "Leaner," she says. The man nods and chooses another piece. I smile proudly at my mother's ability to choose what is best, feel sorry for those families whose mothers don't have the wisdom to say, "Leaner."

Our last stop before going home is the bakery. Arms stretched with bags of groceries, my mother and I sit down for a snack and a cup of tea. There are many bakeries in Chinatown and we try a different one each week. They are all similar, crowded, noisy with sugar-soaked air, and a wall-size selection of cakes and buns. We slide into a booth and my mother orders a curry puff and two cups of tea. I ask for the sponge cake that is shaped in a cone of wax paper. I like to peel back the paper and stroke the bubbly soft inside of the cake.

When our food arrives, I ask my mother, "Did you like curry puffs when you were a little girl?"

"No, when I lived in China, it was on a farm. We did not have cakes. But when I went to Hong Kong, then I liked red bean ice." My mother points to the tent card menu on our table. There is a photo of a parfait glass filled with red bean soup poured over crushed ice and topped with vanilla ice cream.

"In Hong Kong, your father and I were very poor. So, when we went out, your father would order a red bean ice for me and he would drink lemon-flavoured water. Your father is a good man."

After finishing her curry puff, my mother goes to the counter and orders a box of Chinese pastries to take home. She will pack them in my father's lunch.

My daughter cannot sit still on the bus. She crawls back and forth over my lap, interrogates the people around us.

"We have a car, you know. Do you have a car? What's your name?"

She rings the bell twice before our stop. The bus driver glares at me in the rear view mirror.

On the street, I hurry my daughter along. Shuffle her past the slouching addicts, the day-time prostitutes. She ignores my warnings and says hello to a freckled girl in a rabbit fur jacket. The girl waves.

We squeeze through the heavy glass door of the Chinese Centre. On my right hand, my daughter; my left hand balances my purse, her knapsack and her scarf. She runs ahead, then stops and waits for me at my mother's door.

I am struck by the smell as we enter my mother's room. An anti-septic odor tinged with sweetness, as if cleaning products have missed something ripe and sticky under the bed. When I first visited the Centre, I noticed the smell in the rooms of the other patients. I was sure my mother's room would smell different, light, flowery, like our home. I brought in plants and freshening sprays, but the plants disappeared every week and the sprays evaporated.

My daughter cups a hand over her nose and looks up at me with a crinkled grimace. She grips my fingers tight with her other hand as we approach my mother.

I sit in an orange plastic chair beside the bed and set our bags on the floor; my daughter climbs onto my lap. I take my mother's hand in mine. Her hands are bony and crooked, her fingers rough and hard like wood. They make me think of the wicked witches I read about in grade school, with their gnarled, restraining claws.

We speak in Cantonese. I ask my mother how she is. She says that she is fine, but her bones have been aching. My daughter leans back against my chest and clutches my free hand; she is afraid my mother will want to touch her. I tell my daughter to say hello to her grandma, I have taught her to say it in Cantonese, but she remains silent. My mother smiles at my daughter.

"Remember me?" my mother asks.

My daughter squints to understand the unfamiliar language. My mother's hand rises slowly off the bed and floats towards my daughter's face like a hypnotized wooden snake. My daughter presses herself against me as hard as she can, holds her body in complete stillness as my mother strokes her cheek.

"Beautiful girl," my mother whispers. "So beautiful."

My daughter tries to turn her face away from my mother's touch. My mother laughs.

"So shy," she says.

An attendant enters to tidy my mother's room. My mother calls her over.

"Have you met my family?" my mother asks.

"Every time they visit," the attendant jokes.

"She's not very bright," my mother whispers to me.

"Come," my mother says to the attendant, "let me introduce you."

The attendant comes to the bed. We smile apologies at each other.

"This is my daughter," my mother says, taking my daughter's small hand. I watch the soft white skin disappear into my mother's blotchy paw. My daughter is so still; I wonder if she has stopped breathing.

The attendant teases my mother.

"Isn't she a bit young to be your daughter?"

My mother stares at the attendant as if she had just said something very rude.

"Who," the attendant tries again as she points to me, "is this?"

"This is my sister. She came by boat from China to look after my daughter while I am in the hospital."

My mother thinks we are back in Hong Kong. The attendant leaves quietly. I take my mother's hand off my daughter's and hold it in my own.

"Mother, I am your daughter. This is my daughter, your grand-daughter."

My mother smiles and nods her head. I can not tell if she knows she has made a mistake, or if she thinks I have made one, or if she thinks I am playing a joke on her.

There is silence until I speak again. "Are you getting enough to eat?"

My mother gives me a puzzled look, then smiles. I wait for her answer, but she stares at me as if she is waiting for me to speak.

"Mother—"

"You know what they don't have here?"

"What?" I ask with some relief.

Why do writers write? Because it isn't there.

Thomas Berger

"Red bean ice." She smiles a broad smile. "Red bean ice," she says again as she reaches out a wooden finger to tickle my daughter. "Red bean ice."

My daughter tries to sit still, but my mother's finger makes her squirm and giggle.

"Red bean ice."

My daughter cackles and leans forward to try and tickle my mother.

"Red bean ice!" My daughter shouts, though the Chinese words are just sounds to her. "Red bean ice!"

My mother laughs. "Smart girl, smart girl." Her hand pats my daughter's knee.

There is a long silence as my mother smiles at my daughter and my daughter watches my mother's hand on her knee.

My daughter pulls my sleeve. "The book," she whispers. "Get the book."

I dig through her knapsack and find the book she has brought to read to her grandma.

My mother pats the edge of the bed and my daughter climbs up next to her. I note with envy that my daughter's body is still small and can easily fit into small places.

She holds the book halfway between herself and my mother, so my mother can look at the illustrations. She reads a line then points to the corresponding picture. My mother hasn't spoken English for over a year, but she nods on cue each time my daughter looks up at her. My mother strokes my daughter's hair and hums softly. My daughter leans into her and my mother rests her cheek on the top of my daughter's head. My daughter's lips move less and less with each turned page, her eyes close against her will as she trails her small finger under each line of words.

My mother lies back, eyes closed, soothing my daughter into sleep, patting her small thigh in a gentle rhythm. She holds my daughter against her and sings an old Cantonese lullaby. Her thin voice, a sweet, delicate melody.

I curl in my chair. What is this song? What is she remembering? The song that played the night she met my father and removed her new shoes under the table to be respectably shorter than him when she stood? The folk songs my father sang to his pregnant wife to keep her warm as they crossed the muddy choppiness of the Yangtze river on a cargo boat?

Often, my mother forgets she and my father had a child. I am used to being called a nurse or doctor, her best friend. I am not used to the darkness in her eyes when she thinks I am a stranger.

The afternoon light has grown dim with rain clouds. My mother and daughter are a silhouette against the window. They are caught in fairy tale sleep, deep and motionless; I almost believe nothing will wake them. But it is time for us to leave.

I lean forward in my chair, slip my hand under my mother's hand, lift it from my daughter's thigh. I hold my mother's hand in mine, this time feeling its true weight: bones, skin, old muscle. I raise her hand to my cheek and kiss the papery skin of her palm. I climb out of my chair and kneel down on the floor beside her bed. I lay my head on the mattress and press my mother's hand against my face.

I am remembering a rainy day, a crowded bus, my small body stretched across the seat. My head nestled in my mother's lap, her smooth hand stroking my face. The lulling hum of the bus engine. It is a long journey home.

Lunchtime by Gu Xiong. Woodcut

Where is the focal point of this work—to what part of the illustration are your eyes drawn? How does the artist create this focal point? Consider elements such as composition, line, shape, white space, and content.

Nancy Lee, author of poetry and fiction, has won awards for her writing. She works at the SFU Writing and Publishing program as an instructor and is currently writing a collection of short stories called *Dead Girls*.

I. *Response*

a. The plot of "Red Bean Ice" is divided into sections. Create a diagram that visually represents the way the plot is structured. In what way does the plot structure support one of the main ideas in the story?

b. Describe the narrator's behaviour in each section of the story. What inferences can you make about the narrator's character based on this analysis? Do you think the visit to the Chinese Centre was a good idea? Explain.

c. The narrator's husband appears briefly in the story. What is revealed through his presence?

d. Describe your personal reaction to the final section of the story. What mood or moods was the author trying to establish? Did you like the way the story ended and, in your view, was the conclusion effective? Give reasons for your answer.

2. *Literature Studies* *Proverbs* Nancy Lee includes a number of **proverbs** in the flashback segment of the story. Make a list of these proverbs and speculate on the functions they serve within the story. In a small group, brainstorm other proverbs with which you are familiar. Choose one or two of the proverbs that you think express valuable life lessons. Next, create a proverb of your own that captures one of the themes of "Red Bean Ice." Present the results of your discussion to the class.

A **proverb** is a short saying that expresses a basic truth or useful principle.

3. *Writing* *Memoir* Take this opportunity to portray, in writing, a special memory from your own life. Use vivid, descriptive language to capture the details of your experience, and include personal reflections that explain why that particular memory is significant to you. You can choose to share this piece of writing or keep it private.

4. *Making Connections* "Red Bean Ice" and "A Drowning" both focus on important questions that arise when life is ending. In a brief essay, explore how the two works are similar and different in terms of the situations and themes they present.

Fiction keeps its audience by retaining
the world as its subject matter. People like
the world. Many people actually prefer it to art
and spend their days by choice in the thick of it.

—Annie Dillard

Theme Connections

- "*Groom Service,*" a story about mother/child relationships, Vol. I, p. 12
- "*A Drowning,*" a story about the end of a life, Vol. I, p. 160
- "*The Circle Game,*" a song about the inevitability of the passing of time, Vol. I, p. 180
- "*Do Not Go Gentle Into That Good Night,*" a poem that dares one to defy death, Vol. I, p. 209
- "*The Five Stages of Grief,*" a poem detailing the grieving process, Vol. I, p. 215

Poetry

The essentials of poetry are rhythm,
dance, and the human voice.

Earle Birney

If a Poem Could Walk

by Lorna Crozier

It would have paws, not feet,
four of them
to sink into the moss
when humans blunder up the path.

Or hooves, small ones,
leaving half-moons in the sand.
Something to make you stop
                                    and wonder
what kind of animal this is,
10   where it came from, where it's going.

It draws nearest when you are most alone.
You lay red plums on your blanket,
a glass of cool cider, two sugar cubes,

knowing it is tame and wild—
the perfect animal—
knowing it will stop for nothing
as it walks
                    with its four new legs
right off the page

A poem can be many things/in miniature:
a short story/about people
a photograph/a surreal landscape
and perhaps an instant of ecstacy?

—Dorothy Livesay

A poem should be equal to:
Not true.

—Archibald MacLeish

Previous page:
Moon Dream, August by Tim Greyhavens. Iris print on canvas

The Carousel of Time

Life is like a carousel, forever turning and repeating its cycles. In the midst of growth and change, the poet finds opportunities for insight, foresight, and reflection.

I Grew Up

by Lenore Keeshig-Tobias

I

i grew up on the reserve
thinking it was the most
beautiful place in the world

i grew up thinking
i'm never going
to leave this place

i was a child
a child who would
lie under trees

10

watching wind's rhythms
sway leafy boughs
back and forth

back and forth
sweeping it seemed
the clouds into great piles

and rocking me as
i snuggled in the grass
like a bug basking in the sun

II

i grew up on the reserve
thinking it was the most   20
beautiful place in the world

i grew up thinking
i'm never going
to leave this place

i was a child
a child who ran
wild rhythms

through the fields
the streams
the bush   30

eating berries
cupping cool water
to my wild stained mouth

and hiding in the
treetops with
my friends

III

we used to laugh at teachers and
tourists who referred to
our bush as *forests* or *woods*

40 *forests* and *woods*
were places of
fairy-tale text

were places where people,
especially children, got lost
where wild beasts roamed

our bush was where we played
and where the rabbits squirrels
foxes deer and the bear lived

i grew up thinking
i'm never going   50
to leave this place

i grew up on the reserve
thinking it was the most
beautiful place in the world

Boys Playing Football by Allen Sapp. Acrylic on canvas

What specific techniques has the artist used to impart a sense of movement and energy into his painting? What impression do you think he is trying to convey about the game and the setting in which it is taking place?

After the Wedding

by Marisa Anlin Alps

The first time I realized I was Chinese
I was seventeen, travelled east
to Toronto to celebrate my cousin's
marriage, the sole relation
from my branch of the family tree.
I'd never seen so many of my relatives
in one place, their unknown
faces swirling before me
and everyone there was Chinese.

10 Suddenly it hit me and I knew
I was too (or at least half)
a surprise since I've been everything else
for so long.

My mother says she feels more Canadian
than anything else, but perhaps we moved
to the island pockets of the west
coast to emulate her island childhood, a hint
of possibility in the Caribbean accents
slipping so easily around me, a little
20 like those split leaf plants
my grandmother smuggled into Trinidad,
the ones that grew, flourished
took over a whole corner of her lovely
garden and yet, I felt white
for the first time in my life, different
still from everyone around me, especially
during dim sum in Toronto's Chinatown
an intense experience with tripe and
chicken feet and the wonder
30 of what was not said.

After the wedding, long and noisy tables
filled the banquet hall like sunflowers
pushing toward the centre of the dance
floor, couples whirling around the chairs.
My cousin asked me to dance but I was shy,
eyes downcast. *How did he see me?*

dim sum: Chinese
dumplings and other
small delicacies

The flowers scented the air like wine,
voices like music, while others
flew I sat there on the edge, wonder pouring
40   from me, distant from the centre
I did not feel much, but I thought
I am Chinese
horizons shrinking
and changing before my eyes
a second wedding taking place
within me, two
inheritances exchanging vows.

Brian at Eighteen

by Rick Hillis

Brian, 18, spins
the basketball on the axis
of a finger

controls the angle of its revolution
(the crowd gasps)

This is his world
He dribbles it to the top of the key
It throbs the floor by his boot running shoe

& he shields it with his body
10   which is thin in a way
time will make it forget

His bright red uniform sways like a sail
on his bones

in this vacuum of many held breaths

.   .   .

Brian, tired hero of morning
studies his hemisphere on a school library map
until he dreams
his footprints into Mexican sand

His thin body hunches over the world
20   His pencil arcs correctly calculating distance
not time

.   .   .

Brian wears gym shorts
spins the perfect leather world
on the axis of his finger

The bleachers are empty now
the gym hollow

It is June &

Brian feints
drives left, leaps, lets go

30   Ball arcing beneath dimmed lights
across lines & lines until it hits home

circles the rim around

In mid air Brian holds
this pose:

fingers of his right hand flung forward

of his left shielding his eyes
as if fending off a blow

or studying the lines
of his own palm

1. *Response*
   a. Which of the three poems ("I Grew Up," "After the Wedding," or "Brian at Eighteen") were you best able to identify or connect with? Why?
   b. Speculate on the purpose Lenore Keeshig-Tobias may have had in mind when she wrote "I Grew Up." Do you think the poem is autobiographical? Why or why not?
   c. What interpretation would you offer for the last five lines of "After the Wedding"? Explain your interpretation and your reasoning to a partner.
   d. Why do you think Rick Hillis chose to write "Brian at Eighteen"? Why do you think Hillis focusses on these particular moments in Brian's life? Who do you think Brian is?

2. *Making Connections* In a group, compile a list of similarities and differences between "I Grew Up" and "After the Wedding." Consider poetic form and technique, and the possible purpose of the poets, as well as the ideas, feelings, and experiences described.

The Circle Game

by Joni Mitchell

Yesterday a child came out to wonder
Caught a dragonfly inside a jar
Fearful when the sky was full of thunder
And tearful at the falling of a star

Then the child moved ten times round the seasons
Skated over ten clear frozen streams
Words like when you're older must appease him
And promises of someday make his dreams

And the seasons they go round and round
10 And the painted ponies go up and down
We're captive on the carousel of time
We can't return we can only look
Behind from where we came
And go round and round and round
In the circle game

Sixteen springs and sixteen summers gone now
Cartwheels turn to car wheels thru the town
And they tell him take your time it won't be long now
Till you drag your feet to slow the circles down

20 And the seasons they go round and round
And the painted ponies go up and down
We're captive on the carousel of time
We can't return we can only look
Behind from where we came
And go round and round and round
In the circle game

So the years spin by and now the boy is twenty
Though his dreams have lost some grandeur coming true
There'll be new dreams maybe better dreams and plenty
30 Before the last revolving year is through

And the seasons they go round and round
And the painted ponies go up and down
We're captive on the carousel of time
We can't return we can only look
Behind from where we came
And go round and round and round
In the circle game

Poetry is boned with ideas, nerved and blooded
with emotions, all held together by the delicate,
tough skin of words.

—*Paul Engle*

Pride

by Marilyn Cay

he challenges his father
to arm wrestle
and the two ready themselves
at the kitchen table
this time
there is something about the son's calmness
that makes the father insist upon a fair start
his arm tense
the father breaks with speed
10   in order to put his son's arm down soundly

but he meets with iron this time
the two arms tremble, straight up and down
muscles bulging
hands gripping tightly

afterwards the mother says
the father was the big winner
even though it is her son
whose strength prevailed

1. *Response*
   a. Do you think the song "The Circle Game" expresses an optimistic or pessimistic outlook on life? Explain.
   b. In "Pride," the mother says, "the father was the big winner." What do you think she means by this comment?
   c. Reflect on your own life and identify one event that you feel represents an important moment in your growth toward independence. In a piece of personal writing, describe the event and explain what it means to you.

2. *Literature Studies* *Understatement* "Pride" is notable for its understatement. What details or events did the poet choose not to reveal, and how does this contribute to the understatement? In general, why is understatement an effective writing technique?

Silent, but ...

by Tsuboi Shigeji

Translated from the Japanese by Geoffrey Bownan and Anthony Thwaite

I MAY be silent, but
I'm thinking.
I may not talk, but
Don't mistake me for a wall.

There's Silence Between One Page and Another

by Valerio Magrelli

Translated by Jonathan Galassi

There's silence between one page and another.
The long stretch of the land up to the woods
where gathered shadows
exit from the day
and nights show through
discrete and precious
like fruit on branches.
In this luminous
and geographic frenzy
10   I am still unsure
whether to be the landscape I am crossing
or the journey I am making there.

I Know I Am Young

by Ann Lazechko

I know I am young
and need to learn—
but you are old
and need to remember.

On the Value of Fantasies

by Elizabeth Brewster

The teacher on the morning radio program
disapproves because her girl students
have such unrealistic fantasies.
They all think they will go to college,
marry a lawyer or a professor,
have two kids and two cars,
and live happily ever after.

And she gets them to play a game
in which Linda becomes a widow at fifty,
10 Paulette is deserted at thirty-five
and has to bring up four kids
on a steno's salary, and poor Jennifer
never marries at all.
How will they cope?

Of course it's a matter of
one fantasy against another;
and sometimes it's fun
to imagine oneself bearing up against adversity.

Myself, though, I agree with the kids
20 that it's rather a dumb game.
It's true, life is full of these dirty tricks,
but being prepared for the worst may make it happen.

steno's: stenographer's; a stenographer transcribes speech using shorthand writing

(More might be said
for fantasizing about space travel
or maybe about being a mermaid.)

I still hope (two months before my fifty-third birthday)
that I may yet meet that handsome stranger
all the fortunetellers have told me about;
that sometime my lottery ticket
30   will win a tax-free fortune,
and that my poems become household words
and make the next edition of Colombo's *Quotations*.

Colombo's Quotations: a reference work containing quotations by notable Canadians, edited by John Robert Colombo

I might as well believe in heaven, too,
for all the good it will do me to admit
statistics are against it.

1. *Response*

a. "Silent, but …" and "There's Silence Between One Page and Another" express different perspectives on the meaning of silence. Which poem do you prefer? Explain.

b. In your own words, summarize what "On the Value of Fantasies" says about dreams and fantasies. Do you agree with this message? Why or why not?

c. In a group, create a brief oral presentation that shows how each of the four preceding poems has something to say about the theme of personal potential.

2. *Writing* Letter

Write a letter to the teacher described in "On the Value of Fantasies," in which you comment on her point of view. To complete this task, you will need to assume a specific voice. For example, you may choose to pretend you are one of her students or an adult who heard the radio program.

3. *Visual Communication* Illustration

Create an illustration that captures the visual imagery contained in "There's Silence Between One Page and Another." Present your work and explain how it is true to the poem.

The Swimmer's Moment

by Margaret Avison

For everyone
The swimmer's moment at the whirlpool comes,
But many at that moment will not say
"This is the whirlpool, then."
By their refusal they are saved
From the black pit, and also from contesting
The deadly rapids, and emerging in
The mysterious, and more ample, further waters.
And so their bland-blank faces turn and turn
Pale and forever on the rim of suction
They will not recognize.
Of those who dare the knowledge
Many are whirled into the ominous centre
That, gaping vertical, seals up
For them an eternal boon of privacy,
So that we turn away from their defeat
With a despair, not from their deaths, but for
Ourselves, who cannot penetrate their secret
Nor even guess at the anonymous breadth
Where one or two have won:
(The silver reaches of the estuary).

Symposium

by Paul Muldoon

You can lead a horse to water but you can't make it hold
its nose to the grindstone and hunt with the hounds.
Every dog has a stitch in time. Two heads? You've been sold
one good turn. One good turn deserves a bird in the hand.

A bird in the hand is better than no bread.
To have your cake is to pay Paul.
Make hay while you can still hit the nail on the head.
For want of a nail the sky might fall.

People in glass houses can't see the wood
10   for the new broom. Rome wasn't built between two stools.
Empty vessels wait for no man.

A hair of the dog is a friend indeed.
There's no fool like the fool
who's shot his bolt. There's no smoke after the horse is gone.

1. *Response*
    a. "Symposium" is constructed of many different proverbs that have been patched together. Identify and complete as many of the proverbs as you can. In small groups, discuss the meaning of the proverbs and the poem.
    b. Is "Symposium" a sonnet? Give reasons for your answer.
    c. Compose two or three questions that, if answered, would help you better understand the meaning of "The Swimmer's Moment." In a group, try to answer one another's questions. Present your conclusions to the class.

2. *Language Focus* *Proverbs* Using Internet or library resources, find proverbs from a variety of cultures; then write your own poem similar in style to "Symposium." As you select your proverbs, consider the message you wish your poem to convey. Be prepared to share the original completed proverbs. What do you think accounts for the continuing popularity of proverbs?

3. *Oral Language* *Choral Reading* In a small group, prepare an expressive choral reading of either "Symposium" or "The Swimmer's Moment." Your reading should capture the mood of the poem, and be expressive and entertaining. Present your reading to the class.

A poet is someone who is astonished by everything.
—*Anonymous*

The Layers

by Stanley Kunitz

I have walked through many lives,
some of them my own,
and I am not who I was,
though some principle of being
abides, from which I struggle
not to stray.
When I look behind,
as I am compelled to look
before I can gather strength
10 to proceed on my journey,
I see the milestones dwindling
toward the horizon
and the slow fires trailing
from the abandoned camp-sites,
over which scavenger angels
wheel on heavy wings.
Oh, I have made myself a tribe
out of my true affections,
and my tribe is scattered!
20 How shall the heart be reconciled
to its feast of losses?
In a rising wind
the manic dust of my friends,
those who fell along the way,
bitterly stings my face.
Yet I turn, I turn,
exulting somewhat,
with my will intact to go
wherever I need to go,
30 and every stone on the road
precious to me.
In my darkest night,
when the moon was covered
and I roamed through wreckage,
a nimbus-clouded voice
directed me:

"Live in the layers,
not on the litter."
Though I lack the art
40 to decipher it,
no doubt the next chapter
in my book of transformations
is already written.
I am not done with my changes.

Young Soul

by Amiri Baraka (LeRoi Jones)

First, feel, then feel, then
read, or read, then feel, then
fall, or stand, where you
already are. Think
of your self, and the other
selves ... think
of your parents, your mothers
and sisters, your bentslick
father, then feel, or
10 fall, on your knees
if nothing else will move you,

    then read
    and look deeply
    into all matters
    come close to you
    city boys—
    country men

    Make some muscle
    in your head, but
20 use the muscle
    in yr heart

1. **Response**
    a. "The Layers" contains a number of unusual images. Choose any three such images and discuss what ideas and feelings they convey to you.
    b. Examine "Young Soul," noting the way the words are placed on the page. Suggest possible reasons for the unconventional arrangement (remembering that there are no absolutely right or wrong answers).
    c. What does the word *bentslick* (from "Young Soul") suggest to you? Discuss a possible meaning for this invented word.

2. **Literature Studies** *Interpretation* In groups, discuss possible interpretations of these key lines: "Live in the layers,/not on the litter" ("The Layers") and "Make some muscle/in your head, but/use the muscle/in yr heart" ("Young Soul"). It is not your task to convince others of your point of view. Simply share your interpretation and listen carefully to the interpretations of others. Do you think listening to multiple interpretations is a helpful or distracting approach to under-standing poems?

Poetry is important. No less than science,
it seeks a hold upon reality, and the closeness of its
approach is the test of its success.
—*Babette Deutsch*

Theme Connections

for all of the poems in the cluster "The Carousel of Time"
- *"On the Rainy River," a story about making decisions, Vol. I, p. 70*
- *"The Spaces Between Stars," a story about determining one's personal identity, Vol. I, p. 100*
- *"A New Perspective," an essay about growing up with an unwell parent, Vol. II, p. 45*
- *"My Old Newcastle," a memoir about growing up in a particular place, Vol. II, p. 52*
- *"Venus Sucked In," a radio play in which parental and other relationships play an important role, Vol. II, p. 224*

Since Feeling Is First

More than any other literary form, poetry is used for the expression of powerful feelings. The poems that follow explore the complexities of love, passion, and devotion.

Since Feeling Is First

by E. E. Cummings

since feeling is first
who pays any attention
to the syntax of things
will never wholly kiss you;

wholly to be a fool
while Spring is in the world

my blood approves,
and kisses are a better fate
than wisdom
lady i swear by all flowers. Don't cry
—the best gesture of my brain is less than
your eyelids' flutter which says

we are for each other:then
laugh,leaning back in my arms
for life's not a paragraph

and death i think is no parenthesis

Love Is Not All

by Edna St. Vincent Millay

Love is not all: it is not meat nor drink
Nor slumber nor a roof against the rain;
Nor yet a floating spar to men that sink
And rise and sink and rise and sink again;
Love can not fill the thickened lung with breath,
Nor clean the blood, nor set the fractured bone;
Yet many a man is making friends with death
Even as I speak, for lack of love alone.
It well may be that in a difficult hour,
10 Pinned down by pain and moaning for release,
Or nagged by want past resolution's power,
I might be driven to sell your love for peace,
Or trade the memory of this night for food.
It well may be. I do not think I would.

Sonnet CXVI

by William Shakespeare

Let me not to the marriage of true minds
Admit impediments. Love is not love
Which alters when it alteration finds,
Or bends with the remover to remove:—
O no! It is an ever-fixèd mark   **mark:** beacon
That looks on tempests, and is never shaken;
It is the star to every wandering bark,   **wandering bark:**
Whose worth's unknown, although his height be taken.   lost ship

Love's not Time's fool, though rosy lips and cheeks
10 Within his bending sickle's compass come;   **compass:** range
Love alters not with his brief hours and weeks,
But bears it out ev'n to the edge of doom.
If this be error and upon me proved,
I never writ, nor no man ever loved.

Romeo and Juliet by Ford Madox Brown. Oil on canvas

In a group, discuss the archetypes, clichés, and/or stereotypes contained within this visual interpretation of the famous balcony scene from Shakespeare's *Romeo and Juliet*. How does this work compare with Lichtenstein's *Drowning Girl* (p. 201)?

Since Feeling Is First • **193**

1. Response
a. What ideas or sentiments about love are suggested in Cummings' poem "Since Feeling Is First"? How do you feel about these ideas?
b. Shakespeare's "Sonnet CXVI" is a popular choice as a reading at wedding ceremonies. Generate at least three reasons why you think this poem has attained this distinction.
c. Do you think "Love Is Not All" is contradictory in its view of love? Explain.

2. Literature Studies *Comparison* Use a T-chart or other graphic organizer to show the similarities and differences between "Sonnet CXVI" and "Love Is Not All."

3. Writing *Imitation* Rewrite "Love Is Not All," using images and details from your own experience. You may choose to maintain the serious tone or create a humorous parody instead. Maintain the sonnet rhyme scheme and rhythm.

I Wish to Paint My Eyes

Anonymous Egyptian hieroglyphic text (circa 1500 B.C.E.)
Translated by Willis Barnstone

I wish to paint my eyes,
so if I see you, my eyes will glisten.
When I approach you and see your love,
you are richest in my heart.
How pleasant this hour is!
May it extend for me to eternity.

Meeting at Night

by Robert Browning

The grey sea and the long black land;
And the yellow half-moon large and low;
And the startled little waves that leap
In fiery ringlets from their sleep,
As I gain the cove with pushing prow,
And quench its speed i' the slushy sand.

Then a mile of warm sea-scented beach;
Three fields to cross till a farm appears;
A tap at the pane, the quick sharp scratch
10   And blue spurt of a lighted match,
And a voice less loud, thro' its joys and fears,
Than the two hearts beating each to each!

Sonnet XIV (If Thou Must Love Me)

by Elizabeth Barrett Browning

If thou must love me, let it be for nought
Except for love's sake only. Do not say,
"I love her for her smile—her look—her way
Of speaking gently—for a trick of thought
That falls in well with mine, and certes brought   **certes:** surely, certainly
A sense of pleasant ease on such a day."
For these things in themselves, Beloved, may
Be changed, or change for thee—and love, so wrought,
May be unwrought so. Neither love me for
10   Thine own dear pity's wiping my cheeks dry—
A creature might forget to weep, who bore
Thy comfort long, and lose thy love thereby!
But love me for love's sake, that evermore
Thou may'st love on, through love's eternity.

1. *Response*
    a. "I Wish to Paint My Eyes" was written almost 3500 years ago. In what ways are the sentiments expressed in this poem modern? What assumptions did you make about the speaker, and why?
    b. Every line of "Meeting at Night" contains imagery. Classify each of the images according to the sense(s) it appeals to.
    c. "Sonnet XIV" contains a logical argument. Summarize the argument in a few brief sentences.

2. *Research and Inquiry* Robert Browning and Elizabeth Barrett Browning were famous as poets and as a couple. Using online or print resources, compile a list of ten important and interesting facts for each of the Brownings. Do you think the details of their relationship affected the way their poetry was and continues to be regarded? Explain.

3. *Critical Thinking* Many of the poems in this section ("Since Feeling Is First") emphasize the idea that love is or should be eternal. Do you think this idea continues to be important in today's society? Express your answer in the form of a brief opinion piece or as a poem.

> Poetry asks people to have values, form opinions, care about some other part of experience besides making money and being successful on the job.
> —*Toi Derricotte*

The Passionate Shepherd to His Love

by Christopher Marlowe

Come live with me and be my Love,
And we will all the pleasures prove
That hills and valleys, dale and field,
And all the craggy mountains yield.

There will we sit upon the rocks
And see the shepherds feed their flocks,
By shallow rivers, to whose falls
Melodious birds sing madrigals.

madrigals: love songs

There will I make thee beds of roses
10   And a thousand fragrant posies,
A cap of flowers, and a kirtle
Embroidered all with leaves of myrtle.

kirtle: a dress or skirt

A gown made of the finest wool,
Which from our pretty lambs we pull,
Fair linèd slippers for the cold,
With buckles of the purest gold.

A belt of straw and ivy buds
With coral clasps and amber studs:
And if these pleasures may thee move,
20   Come live with me and be my Love.

Thy silver dishes for thy meat
As precious as the gods do eat,
Shall on an ivory table be
Prepared each day for thee and me.

The shepherd swains shall dance and sing
For thy delight each May-morning:
If these delights thy mind may move,
Then live with me and be my Love.

swains: lads

The Nymph's Reply to the Shepherd

by Sir Walter Raleigh

If all the world and love were young,
And truth in every shepherd's tongue,
These pretty pleasures might me move,
To live with thee and be thy love.

Time drives the flocks from field to fold,   **fold:** a fenced enclosure
When rivers rage, and rocks grow cold;
And Philomel becometh dumb;   **Philomel:** the nightingale
The rest complains of cares to come.

The flowers do fade, and wanton fields
10 To wayward winter reckoning yields;
A honey tongue, a heart of gall,
Is fancy's spring, but sorrow's fall.

Thy gowns, thy shoes, thy beds of roses,
Thy cap, thy kirtle, and thy posies,
Soon break, soon wither, soon forgotten;
In folly ripe, in reason rotten.

Thy belt of straw and ivy buds,
Thy coral clasps and amber studs,
All these in me no means can move,
20 To come to thee and be thy love.

But could youth last, and love still breed,
Had joys no date, nor age no need,
Then these delights my mind might move
To live with thee and be thy love.

1. Response
Discuss both Marlowe's "The Passionate Shepherd to His Love" and Raleigh's "The Nymph's Reply to the Shepherd," and their contrasting views of love.

2. Literature Studies *Persona* What **persona** does Sir Walter Raleigh use in his reply to "The Passionate Shepherd to His Love"? In "The Nymph's Reply to the Shepherd," it is easy to distinguish between the poet and the speaker of the poem. Find a poem in this unit in which it is not clear whether the speaker is a persona or the poet him or herself. Why do you think it is an accepted critical practice to assume that the voice of the speaker of a poem is *not* necessarily the poet's own voice?

> The **persona** is the voice or character that represents the narrator in a literary work. A persona is often described as a mask an author deliberately puts on in order to narrate a particular story or poem.

3. Drama *Dialogue* In a group, prepare and present a dramatic reading of the two poems. In your reading, consider the poems as two sides of a single dialogue. You might use music, lighting, movement, and/or costume to enhance your work. Present your reading either as a live or videotaped performance.

4. Focus on Context In *pastoral verse,* such as the two poems above, urban poets idealized life in the country, depicting happy shepherds playing music underneath the trees and pledging their undying love. Discuss this concept and these two examples.

Identify two or three areas of life that people tend to idealize today. How are these ideals expressed in our culture, and in what ways are they realistic or unrealistic?

Poetry is a matter of life,
not just a matter of language.
—*Lucille Clifton*

Variations on the Word Love

by Margaret Atwood

This is a word we use to plug
holes with. It's the right size for those warm
blanks in speech, for those red heart-
shaped vacancies on the page that look nothing
like real hearts. Add lace
and you can sell
it. We insert it also in the one empty
space on the printed form
that comes with no instructions. There are whole
10   magazines with not much in them
but the word *love*, you can
rub it all over your body and you
can cook with it too. How do we know
it isn't what goes on at the cool
debaucheries of slugs under damp
pieces of cardboard? As for the weed-
seedlings nosing their tough snouts up
among the lettuces, they shout it.
Love! Love! sing the soldiers, raising
20   their glittering knives in salute.
Then there's the two
of us. This word
is far too short for us, it has only
four letters, too sparse
to fill those deep bare
vacuums between the stars
that press on us with their deafness.
It's not love we don't wish
to fall into, but that fear.
30   This word is not enough, but it will
have to do. It's a single
vowel in this metallic
silence, a mouth that says
O again and again in wonder
and pain, a breath, a finger-
grip on a cliffside. You can
hold on or let go.

Drowning Girl by Roy Lichtenstein.

In your view, what is the tone of this work? Refer to the style of both the painting and the text in the speech balloon, in your answer. Given that this work is considered Pop Art, what might some characteristics of the Pop Art style be? Do some research to confirm whether your suggestions are correct.

First Person Demonstrative

by Phyllis Gotlieb

I'd rather
heave half a brick than say
I love you, though I do
I'd rather
crawl in a hole than call you
darling, though you are
I'd rather
wrench off an arm than hug you
    though
10 it's what I long to do
I'd rather
gather a posy of poison ivy than
ask if you love me
so if my
hair doesn't stand on end it's
    because
I never tease it
and if my
heart isn't in my mouth it's
20   because
it knows its place
and if I
don't take a bite of your ear
    it's because
gristle gripes my guts
and if you
miss the message better get new
glasses and read it twice

I. Response
a. What observations and objections does Atwood raise about the use of the word *love* in "Variations on the Word *Love*"? Do you agree or disagree with her viewpoint? Explain.
b. What words would you use to describe the **tone** of "Variations on the Word *Love*"? Of "First Person Demonstrative"? How do these poems compare to most of the previous love poems in this section, in terms of tone? Which tone do you prefer, and why?

Tone is the implied attitude of the writer toward the subject or the audience.

2. Writing *Poem* Study the structure of "First Person Demonstrative" carefully to note how the speaker expresses her or his love. Then write your own poem, following the original structure as closely as possible, using unconventional images of your own. You can retain the original first line and the last three lines.

3. Media *Magazine Analysis* What point do you think Atwood is trying to make when she says, "There are whole/magazines with not much in them/but the word *love* ..." Use an issue of a current popular magazine to support your interpretation of this line.

I write poetry in order to live more fully.
—*Judith Rodriguez*

Theme Connections

for all of the poems in the cluster "Since Feeling Is First"
• *"Transients in Arcadia," a story about a couple in love, Vol. I, p. 37*
• *"The Spaces Between Stars," a story about relationship problems, Vol. I, p. 100*
• *"Touching Bottom," a story in which a character falls in and out of love, Vol. I, p. 124*
• *"The Raft," a burlesque act about a couple's first meeting, Vol. II, p. 207*

Dover Beach

by Matthew Arnold

The sea is calm to-night.
The tide is full, the moon lies fair
Upon the Straits;—on the French coast, the light
Gleams, and is gone; the cliffs of England stand,
Glimmering and vast, out in the tranquil bay.
Come to the window, sweet is the night air!
Only, from the long line of spray
Where the sea meets the moon-blanched sand,
Listen! you hear the grating roar

10   Of pebbles which the waves suck back, and fling,
At their return, up the high strand,
Begin, and cease, and then again begin,
With tremulous cadence slow, and bring
The eternal note of sadness in.

Sophocles long ago
Heard it on the Ægæan, and it brought
Into his mind the turbid ebb and flow,
Of human misery; we
Find also in the sound a thought,

20   Hearing it by this distant northern sea.

The sea of faith
Was once, too, at the full, and round earth's shore
Lay like the folds of a bright girdle furled;
But now I only hear
Its melancholy, long, withdrawing roar,
Retreating to the breath
Of the night-wind down the vast edges drear
And naked shingles of the world.

Ah, love, let us be true

30   To one another! for the world, which seems
To lie before us like a land of dreams,
So various, so beautiful, so new,
Hath really neither joy, nor love, nor light,
Nor certitude, nor peace, nor help for pain;

moon-blanched: whitened or made pale by moonlight

Sophocles: ancient Greek dramatist (496–406 B.C.E.), author of *Oedipus Rex* and *Antigone*

girdle: a belt or sash

shingles: large, smooth stones; beaches consisting of such stones

And we are here as on a darkling plain
Swept with confused alarms of struggle and flight,
Where ignorant armies clash by night.

If There Be Sorrow

by Mari Evans

If there be sorrow
let it be
for things undone
undreamed
   unrealized
       unattained

to these add one:
love withheld
   restrained

1. Response
   a. According to the speaker of "Dover Beach," what is the
   importance of love? Would you call this poem a celebration
   of love? Why or why not?
   b. Choose one phrase or image from "Dover Beach" that
   you think captures the atmosphere of the poem best.
   c. Look carefully at the way in which both Arnold and Evans
   use rhyme in their poems. What similarities and differences
   do you see? Did you notice the presence of rhyme in these
   poems when you read them the first time? Do you think the
   poets have used rhyme effectively? Explain.

2. Focus on Context "Dover Beach" is widely considered to
   be one of the classics of English poetry. Using Internet or
   print resources, research this poem's place in our cultural
   history. Why do critics consider it to be so important? In
   a contemporary Canadian classroom, is this poem still
   important?

Grief of Mind

What pain can be greater than grief? These poems examine
thoughts and emotions associated with mortality and loss.
Some look beyond the limits of our knowledge, searching for
purpose, peace, and hope.

Late Landing

by Julia M. Spicher

It's 1:30 and raining
as we wake above Pittsburgh,
but we feel back in Paris
asleep in hotel beds
dreaming of a rusty-lipped stewardess,
the long, black Atlantic
and naps in foam seats
that recline just so far.

We walk drugged, down the ramp
10   like game-show contestants
to an audience of parents,
wide waves and broad smiles.

Mom hugs me too hard
and wipes at her cheek—
was nine days that long?
I tell her I loved it,
did you get my postcards?
we drank coffee from bowls there,
and headlights were yellow,
20   Dad's in the car?

The wet trunk lid slams
and wipers start whining.
I shiver cold and numb.
Mom leans over the seat
and sighs for her secret,
"On the day that you left
Grandpa died."

The Chariot (Because I Could Not Stop for Death)

by Emily Dickinson

Because I could not stop for Death—
He kindly stopped for me—
The Carriage held but just ourselves—
And Immortality.

We slowly drove—He knew no haste,
And I had put away
My labour and my leisure too,
For His Civility—

We passed the School, where Children strove
10 At Recess—in the Ring—
We passed the Fields of Gazing Grain—
We passed the Setting Sun—

Or rather—He passed Us—
The Dews grew quivering and chill—
For only Gossamer, my Gown—
My Tippet—only Tulle—

Tippet: a covering for the shoulders

Tulle: a fine netting used for veils and other clothing

We paused before a House that seemed
A Swelling of the Ground—
The Roof was scarcely visible—
20 The Cornice—in the Ground.

Cornice: moulding at the top of a wall

Since then—'tis Centuries—and yet
Feels shorter than the Day
I first surmised the Horses' Heads
Were toward Eternity—

Miss Dickinson Goes to the Office

by Gail White

Because I could not stop for lunch,
   it kindly stopped for me.
The lunch tray held a lemon sponge   **sponge:** sponge cake
   and watercress and tea.

I heard a fly buzz—in the Slaw—
   immortal for an hour.
The tea was hot—a small Brazil—
   although the cream was sour.

Since then 'tis centuries, yet each
10   seems shorter than the day
I first surmised the weekend was
   five working days away.

1. Response

a. Explain the significance of the title "Late Landing" and how effectively it reflects or reveals the poem.

b. Dickinson's "The Chariot" contains an unusual characterization of Death. In a group, complete a character sketch of Death as portrayed in the poem. What is the tone of this poem?

c. What aspects of "The Chariot" does Gail White imitate in her parody, "Miss Dickinson Goes to the Office"? Discuss the effectiveness and effect of this parody.

d. What does White's poem reveal about death or grieving?

2. Literature Studies

Atmosphere What details in "Late Landing" establish an atmosphere that is appropriate to the "secret" of the last two lines? Refer to specific words and phrases in your answer.

3. *Focus on Context* In a group, conduct some research on the poet Emily Dickinson. Create a mini-biography that summarizes what you feel are the ten most important details about her life and experience as a poet. As well, find a copy of the original published version of "The Chariot" and compare it to the version printed here. Which version do you prefer, and why?

Do Not Go Gentle Into That Good Night

by Dylan Thomas

Do not go gentle into that good night,
Old age should burn and rave at close of day;
Rage, rage against the dying of the light.

Though wise men at their end know dark is right,
Because their words had forked no lightning they
Do not go gentle into that good night.

Good men, the last wave by, crying how bright
Their frail deeds might have danced in a green bay,
Rage, rage against the dying of the light.

10   Wild men who caught and sang the sun in flight,
And learn, too late, they grieved it on its way,
Do not go gentle into that good night.

Grave men, near death, who see with blinding sight
Blind eyes could blaze like meteors and be gay,
Rage, rage against the dying of the light.

And you, my father, there on that sad height,
Curse, bless, me now with your fierce tears, I pray.
Do not go gentle into that good night.
Rage, rage against the dying of the light.

from *He Went Gentle*

by Geraldine Rubia

He went 'gentle into that good night'
and I would not wish it otherwise
for gentle he doubtless came
from that other night
his mother being oh so gentle
or, more precise, unruffleable,
and more or less gentle flowed his life.

Not all went well, far from it,
but the 'slings and arrows' evoked from him
10 no more than a shrug and a wry smile,
and though some would suggest
he forged the slings and arrows himself
who knows that it could have been
any other way.

Humor he had plenty of, though not
the rambunctious kind;
rather the kind that said to one
who smashed a glass on the kitchen floor
"Why wait till you had it washed and dried?"
20 That was it, really, in a nutshell;
it was always the irony he saw, never the tragedy.
Is there any tragedy after all
but the tragedy of no sense of humor?

1. Response
   a. Discuss the organization and structure of Dylan Thomas's "Do Not Go Gentle Into That Good Night."
   b. Reread the last three lines of Rubia's "He Went Gentle" and express the meaning in your own words.
   c. What significant similarities and differences are there in the ideas and feelings expressed in "Do Not Go Gentle Into That Good Night" and "He Went Gentle"? Which poem do you prefer? Why?

2. **Oral Language** *Group Discussion* Verses 2–5 of "Do Not Go Gentle Into That Good Night" deal with the ways in which different types of people approach death. In a group discussion, clarify who these people are and describe the ways in which they approach death. Present your ideas to the class.

3. **Focus on Context** Using Internet or print resources, research the circumstances surrounding the writing of Thomas's "Do Not Go Gentle Into That Good Night." Does your response to the poem change as a result of the information you discovered? Explain.

The World

by Kathleen Raine

It burns in the void.
Nothing upholds it.
Still it travels.

Travelling the void
Upheld by burning
Nothing is still.

Burning it travels.
The void upholds it.
Still it is nothing.

10   Nothing it travels
A burning void
Upheld by stillness.

Reservoir Nocturne by Max Ferguson. Oil on panel

Do you think that this work is an appropriate companion piece to the poem "Acquainted With the Night"? In your answer, refer to specific elements of the photo and the poem.

Acquainted With the Night

by Robert Frost

I have been one acquainted with the night.
I have walked out in rain—and back in rain.
I have outwalked the furthest city light.

I have looked down the saddest city lane.
I have passed by the watchman on his beat
And dropped my eyes, unwilling to explain.

I have stood still and stopped the sound of feet
When far away an interrupted cry
Came over houses from another street,

10 But not to call me back or say good-by;
And further still at an unearthly height,
One luminary clock against the sky

Proclaimed the time was neither wrong nor right.
I have been one acquainted with the night.

Grief of Mind

by Edward de Vere, 17th Earl of Oxford

What plague is greater than the grief of mind?
  The grief of mind that eats in every vein;
In every vein that leaves such clots behind;
  Such clots behind as breed such bitter pain;
So bitter pain that none shall ever find,
What plague is greater than the grief of mind.

ABC

by Robert Pinsky

Any body can die, evidently. Few
Go happily, irradiating joy,

Knowledge, love. Most
Need oblivion, painkillers,
Quickest respite.

Sweet time unafflicted,
Various world:
X = your zenith.

1. Response

a. "Acquainted With the Night" describes the speaker's physical experiences very carefully, but leaves his/her state of mind unspoken. What thoughts or concerns might be responsible for taking the speaker repeatedly out into the night? Compare your ideas with those of a few classmates.

b. Select two of the four preceding poems and explain how the authors use repetition. Evaluate whether that repetition is appropriate and effective.

c. In groups, discuss the possible interpretations of the last line of Pinsky's poem "ABC."

2. Literature Studies *Enjambment* Identify examples of **enjambment** within "Acquainted With the Night." Prepare an oral reading of the poem that reflects the way enjambment affects the rhythm. Why do you think poets use enjambment in their work?

Enjambment occurs when there is no strong punctuation at the end of a line of poetry, allowing a phrase or sentence to carry through that line and into the next without a pause.

3. Vocabulary Using a word web, explore the meaning and connotations of the word *acquainted*. How does the meaning of this word help to shape the meaning of "Acquainted With the Night"? Use a thesaurus or other reference resource and list other words Frost could have used. For each of these alternatives, write a sentence explaining how the word might alter the poem's effect.

4. Writing *ABC Poem* Create a poem of your own that uses the same structure as Pinsky's "ABC." If necessary, use a dictionary or Internet resources to find interesting and unusual words for each letter of the alphabet. Remember that your poem, like Pinsky's, must develop one theme or topic. Ask a classmate to check the grammatical correctness of your work. What were the challenges you faced in writing this poem?

Poetry is a way of taking life by the throat.
—*Robert Frost*

The Five Stages of Grief

by Linda Pastan

The night I lost you
someone pointed me towards
the Five Stages of Grief.
Go that way, they said,
it's easy, like learning to climb
stairs after the amputation.
And so I climbed.
Denial was first.
I sat down at breakfast
10   carefully setting the table
for two. I passed you the toast—
you sat there. I passed
you the paper—you hid
behind it.
Anger seemed more familiar.
I burned the toast, snatched
the paper and read the headlines myself.
But they mentioned your departure,
and so I moved on to
20   *Bargaining.* What could I exchange
for you? The silence
after storms? My typing fingers?
Before I could decide, *Depression*
came puffing up, a poor relation
its suitcase tied together
with string. In the suitcase
were bandages for the eyes
and bottles of sleep. I slid
all the way down the stairs
30   feeling nothing.
And all the time Hope
flashed on and off
in defective neon.
Hope was a signpost pointing
straight in the air.
Hope was my uncle's middle name,
he died of it.

After a year I am still climbing,
though my feet slip
40 on your stone face.
The treeline
has long since disappeared;
green is a colour
I have forgotten.
But now I see what I am climbing
towards: *Acceptance*
written in capital letters,
a special headline:
Acceptance,
50 its name in lights.
I struggle on,
waving and shouting.
Below, my whole life spreads its surf,
all the landscapes I've ever known
or dreamed of. Below
a fish jumps: the pulse
in your neck.
Acceptance. I finally
reach it.
60 But something is wrong.
Grief is a circular staircase.
I have lost you.

Insouciance

by John W. Dickson

If the craven crow and the fierce-eyed hawk
        Swoop over the plain of my wasted years
And the bright plans dwindle to fancy talk
        And hope is restrained by a thousand fears,
Mrs. Brady would dash up the walk waving recipes
for fried crow and hawk stew and ask me to speak
at her Women's Club luncheon.

If Life throws up on my outstretched hand
    And Fate kicks the buttocks of my dreams
10 And my heart becomes a desert land
    Strewn with the bones of famished schemes,
Mrs. Brady would remark that there is so much of
that intestinal flu going around these days and
spend all afternoon showing me how bone chips can
make a delightful center-piece.

If the sun fades out in the black soot sky
    And the reaper comes, as he surely must,
Death-shroud draped over empty eye,
    Reducing endless time to dust,
20 Mrs. Brady would haggle with him a while and
finally agree to pay two dollars for the job
provided he doesn't forget that patch of grass
behind the garage and is sure to trim along the walk.

The Largest Life

by Archibald Lampman

There is a beauty at the goal of life,
A beauty growing since the world began,
Through every age and race, through lapse and strife
Till the great human soul complete her span.
Beneath the waves of storm that lash and burn,
The currents of blind passion that appal,
To listen and keep watch till we discern
The tide of sovereign truth that guides it all;
So to address our spirits to the height,
10 And so attune them to the valiant whole,
That the great light be clearer for our light,
And the great soul the stronger for our soul:
To have done this is to have lived, though fame
Remember us with no familiar name.

1. Response

a. In "The Five Stages of Grief," Pastan uses imagery and figurative language to suggest what the speaker is feeling through the five stages of grief. For each stage, offer your own interpretation of what the speaker is experiencing. What conclusion does the speaker reach at the end of the journey? Do you think the poem ends on an optimistic or pessimistic note? Explain.

b. What does the word *insouciance* mean? How does Dickson use juxtaposition within the poem to bring that meaning to life? Consider both the form of the poem and its content in your answer.

c. Express the theme and message of Lampman's sonnet "The Largest Life" in your own words. Be concise; do not translate the poem line by line.

2. Drama

Dramatization In a group, prepare and present a dramatization of "Insouciance." Through your reading, you should be able to create distinct personalities for the two outlooks on life that are present in each verse. You might also introduce the figures of the crow, the hawk, Life, Death, and Mrs. Brady into your dramatization.

3. Visual Communication

Create a collage or PowerPoint presentation that captures the essence of some of your favourite poems in this section ("Grief of Mind"). Your work should contain appropriate visuals, brief quotations from the poems, and a personal commentary that reflects your own perspective.

Theme Connections

for all of the poems in the cluster "Grief of Mind"

- *"A Drowning," a story about a man drowning, Vol. I, p. 160*
- *"Red Bean Ice," a story about an aging woman, Vol. I, p. 164*
- *"Pierre Trudeau: He Has Gone to His Grace," a tribute to someone who has passed away, page Vol. II, p. 55, and other essays in the cluster "In Memory Of"*
- *"The Dashwoods' Fate Is Decided," a movie script which involves the death of a father, Vol. II, p. 199*

The Good Life

What is the secret of the good life? What obstacles stand in the way of a good life?

The World Is Too Much With Us

by William Wordsworth

The world is too much with us; late and soon,
Getting and spending, we lay waste[1] our powers:
Little we see in Nature that is ours;
We have given our hearts away, a sordid boon![2]
This Sea that bares her bosom to the moon;
The winds that will be howling at all hours,
And are up-gathered now like sleeping flowers;
For this, for everything, we are out of tune;
It moves us not—Great God! I'd rather be
10   A Pagan suckled in a creed outworn;[3]
So might I, standing on this pleasant lea,[4]
Have glimpses that would make me less forlorn;
Have sight of Proteus[5] rising from the sea;
Or hear old Triton[6] blow his wreathèd horn.

[1]**lay waste:** destroy
[2]**boon:** benefit
[3]**suckled in a creed outworn:** raised to believe an obsolete religion
[4]**lea:** meadow
[5]**Proteus:** a Greek sea-god who could change his shape
[6]**Triton:** a Greek sea-god often portrayed with a trident and a seashell horn

Modern Edifices

by Maria Holod

In concrete, in iron,
up the stairs of stone,
between escalators
and elevators
in blinding neon
my world lost its way.
   Smoky windows,
      Smoky sky
   for my world.
10 Artificially cool
air soaked
in metallic smell
spins around my world.
   My papery world
    my world in machines
    my world in digits
    my world, my world
At one time
my world was
20 in the sun
in the sky
in trees and birds
and in human beings.

1. *Response*

a. "The World Is Too Much With Us" and "Modern Edifices" make a similar criticism about modern life. Explain that criticism in your own words.

b. Which poem do you prefer? Explain.

2. *Film Studies* Imagine you are a screenwriter who wants to develop a movie that would communicate the theme of these poems. What story could you tell to bring that theme to life? How could you create a movie with mass appeal on this theme? Create a **synopsis** that would convince a producer to go ahead with the movie. Your synopsis should give the basic storyline, and as well, it might suggest a title and possible cast members.

A **synopsis** provides an overview or summary of a longer work.

3. *Focus on Context* William Wordsworth was an English Romantic poet. Using Internet or print resources, research the characteristics and major themes of the Romantic poets. Focus especially on how they felt about the city. Did researching the context of this poem help you to better appreciate or understand Wordsworth's sonnet? Explain.

When you write in prose you say what you mean.
When you write in rhyme you say what you must.
—*Oliver Wendell Holmes*

Kindly Unhitch That Star, Buddy

by Ogden Nash

I hardly suppose I know anybody who wouldn't rather be a
    success than a failure,
Just as I suppose every piece of crabgrass in the garden would
    much rather be an azalea,
And in celestial circles all the run-of-the-mill angels would
    rather be archangels or at least cherubim and seraphim,[1]
And in the legal world all the little process-servers hope to
    grow up into great big bailiffim and sheriffim.[2]
Indeed, everybody wants to be a wow,
But not everybody knows exactly how.
Some people think they will eventually wear diamonds instead
    of rhinestones
Only by everlastingly keeping their noses to their ghrinestones,
And other people think they will be able to put in more time
    at Palm Beach and the Ritz
By not paying too much attention to attendance at the office
    but rather in being brilliant by starts and fits.
Some people after a full day's work sit up all night getting a
    college education by correspondence,
While others seem to think they'll get just as far by devoting
    their evenings to the study of the difference in temperament
    between brunettance and blondance.
In short, the world is filled with people trying to achieve
    success,
And half of them think they'll get it by saying No and half of
    them by saying Yes,
And if all the ones who say No said Yes, and vice versa, such
    is the fate of humanity that ninety-nine percent of them
    still wouldn't be any better off than they were before,
Which perhaps is just as well because if everybody was a success
    nobody could be contemptuous of anybody else and
    everybody would start in all over again trying to be a
    bigger success than everybody else so they would have
    somebody to be contemptuous of and so on forevermore,
Because when people start hitching their wagons to a star,
That's the way they are.

---

[1]**cherubim and seraphim:** in the Bible, high-ranking angels
[2]**bailiffim and sheriffim:** wordplay on the legal terms *bailiff* and *sheriff*

To Be of Use

by Marge Piercy

The people I love the best
jump into work head first
without dallying in the shallows
and swim off with sure strokes almost out of sight.
They seem to become natives of that element,
the black sleek heads of seals
bouncing like half-submerged balls.

I love people who harness themselves, an ox to a heavy cart,
who pull like water buffalo, with massive patience,
10   who strain in the mud and the muck to move things forward,
who do what has to be done, again and again.

I want to be with people who submerge
in the task, who go into the fields to harvest
and work in a row and pass the bags along,
who are not parlor generals[1] and field deserters[2]
but move in a common rhythm
when the food must come in or the fire be put out.

The work of the world is common as mud.
Botched, it smears the hands, crumbles to dust.
20   But the thing worth doing well done
has a shape that satisfies, clean and evident.
Greek amphoras[3] for wine or oil,
Hopi[4] vases that held corn, are put in museums
but you know they were made to be used.
The pitcher cries for water to carry
and a person for work that is real.

---

[1]**parlor generals:** generals who avoid the battlefield
[2]**field deserters:** soldiers who flee during battle
[3]**amphoras:** two-handled jars
[4]**Hopi:** Aboriginal people of northeast Arizona

Thoughts

by Marty Robillard

There are so many things in life I want to do:
But some I don't have the courage to do,
Some I don't have the ability to do,
And others nobody will let me do.
    So I fish.

1. **Response**
   a. What aspect of life does Nash poke fun at in "Kindly Unhitch That Star, Buddy"? Explain how the title of the poem makes an important contribution to its meaning.
   b. Select three images from "To Be of Use" that you think best capture the speaker's attitude toward work. Be prepared to explain your choices to the class.
   c. Do you agree with the basic message in Marty Robillard's poem "Thoughts"? Why or why not?

2. **Critical Thinking** In a brief essay, show how "To Be of Use" might be regarded as a response to "Kindly Unhitch That Star, Buddy." Use quotations from both poems as evidence to support your argument.

3. **Language Conventions** *Sentence Structure* Examine the punctuation in the final stanza of "Kindly Unhitch That Star, Buddy." How many sentences does the stanza contain? What is the technical term for this construction, and do you think it occurs accidentally or intentionally? Repunctuate the final stanza to correct it, and explain whether you think the poem is improved as a result.

> You will not find poetry anywhere
> unless you bring some of it with you.
> —*Joseph Joubert*

I Am a Rock

by Paul Simon

A winter's day
In a deep and dark December—
I am alone
Gazing from my window
To the streets below
On a freshly fallen silent shroud of snow.
I am a rock;
I am an island.

I build walls,
10   A fortress deep and mighty
That none may penetrate.
I have no need of friendship;
Friendship causes pain.
Its laughter and its loving I disdain.
I am a rock;
I am an island.

Don't talk of love.
Well, I've heard the word before;
It's sleeping in my memory.
20   I won't disturb the slumber
Of feelings that have died.
If I'd never loved, I never would have cried.
I am a rock;
I am an island.

I have my books
And my poetry to protect me.
I am shielded in my armour,
Hiding in my room,
Safe within my tomb.
30   I touch no one and no one touches me.
I am a rock;
I am an island.

And a rock feels no pain,
And an island never cries.

The World Is Not a Pleasant Place to Be

by Nikki Giovanni

the world is not a pleasant place
to be without
someone to hold and be held by

a river would stop
its flow if only
a stream were there
to receive it

an ocean would never laugh
if clouds weren't there
10   to kiss her tears

the world is not
a pleasant place to be without
someone

1. *Response*

a. What advice would you give to the speaker in "I Am a
Rock"? Explain why you think that particular advice is
appropriate.

b. Add two additional stanzas of your own to "The World
Is Not a Pleasant Place to Be." Your stanzas can be inserted
anywhere after the first verse and should be crafted to fit
the structure and language of the poem. Comment on any
insights you gained about the poem through this exercise.

2. *Making Connections* Simon's song lyric "I Am a Rock" was inspired by a quotation from the English poet, John Donne (1572–1631):

> No man is an island, entire of itself; every man is a piece of the continent, a part of the main; if a clod be washed away by the sea, Europe is the less, as well as if a promontory were, as well as if a manor of thy friend's or of thine own were; any man's death diminishes me, because I am involved in mankind; and therefore never send to know for whom the bell tolls; it tolls for thee.

What is Donne saying? How does the above quotation influence your interpretation of Simon's song?

3. *Language Conventions* *Punctuation and Capitalization* Examine "I Am a Rock" and discuss how it uses punctuation and capitalization. What are the general rules for capitalization within poems? Compare the punctuation and capitalization in "I Am a Rock" with that in "The World Is Not a Pleasant Place to Be." What is the effect of the punctuation and capitalization in each poem?

> Poets aren't very useful
> Because they aren't consumeful or produceful.
> —*Ogden Nash*

Theme Connections

for all of the poems in the cluster "The Good Life"
- *"Groom Service," a story in which characters seek to improve their lives through the right marriage, Vol. I, p. 12*
- *"The Shining Houses," a story in which the characters seek to improve their lives at the expense of others, Vol. I, p. 26*
- *"Transients in Arcadia," a story in which the characters seek the good life, Vol. I, p. 37*
- *"A Pair of Silk Stockings," a story in which a character seeks a luxurious escape from her everyday drudgery, Vol. I, p. 86*
- *"Thoughts on Education," an essay that argues for improving one's life through public education, Vol. II, p. 68*

I'm Sorry Says the Machine

by Eve Merriam

I'm sorry says the machine,
Thank you for waiting says the tape recording,
Trying to connect you says the voice in the
      vacuum at the end of the line.

I'm sorry that sister is not in working order.
Please verify your brother and try him again.
I'm sorry that mother is out of service.
Thank you for waiting, that father you have
      reached is a temporary disconnect.

10   I'm sorry that landlord is not in working order.
Please verify your neighborhood and try it again.
I'm sorry those repairs are out of service.
Thank you for waiting, that official you have
      reached is not reachable at this time.

I'm sorry that water is not in drinking order.
Please verify that sunlight and try it later.
I'm sorry that blue sky is out of service.
Thank you for waiting, those flowers and trees
      are permanently disconnected.

20   I'm sorry that country is not in working order.
I'm sorry that planet is out of service.
Please verify that godhead and try much later.
Thank you for waiting, that universe has been
      dis—.

All Watched Over by Machines of Loving Grace

by Richard Brautigan

I like to think (and
the sooner the better!)
of a cybernetic meadow
where mammals and computers
live together in mutually
programming harmony
like pure water
touching clear sky.

I like to think
10   (right now, please!)
of a cybernetic forest
filled with pines and electronics
where deer stroll peacefully
past computers
as if they were flowers
with spinning blossoms.

I like to think
    (it has to be!)
of a cybernetic ecology
20   where we are free of our labors
and joined back to nature,
returned to our mammal
brothers and sisters,
and all watched over
by machines of loving grace.

1. Response
   a. How does Merriam craft "I'm Sorry Says the Machine" so that it builds to a climax? Did you like the way the poem ended? Why or why not?
   b. How do you read "All Watched Over by Machines of Loving Grace"? Do you take it at face value or read it ironically, or does it seem like an interesting but unrealistic vision of the future? Share your perspective on the poem in a group discussion.

2. Making Connections In what significant ways are the ideas and feelings expressed in "I'm Sorry Says the Machine" and "All Watched Over by Machines of Loving Grace" similar and/or different? Conclude your comparison with a statement about which poem you prefer and why.

3. Research and Inquiry Search current media works, either print or electronic, to find two reports on the effect of technology on the human or natural environment. One report should highlight a negative effect, the other a positive effect. Search especially for information "off the beaten path"—information that is not common knowledge (but be sure to verify the accuracy of this information). Present your findings to your classmates. As a class, you might create a technology bulletin board to display the information you gather.

Poetry is the journal of a sea animal living on land, wanting to fly in the air.
   —*Carl Sandburg*

When I Heard the Learn'd Astronomer

by Walt Whitman

When I heard the learn'd astronomer,
When the proofs, the figures, were ranged in columns before me,
When I was shown the charts and diagrams, to add, divide,
    and measure them,
When I sitting heard the astronomer where he lectured
    with much applause in the lecture-room,
How soon unaccountable I became tired and sick,
Till rising and gliding out I wander'd off by myself,
In the mystical moist night-air, and from time to time,
Look'd up in perfect silence at the stars.

Advice to the Young

by Miriam Waddington

1
keep bees and
grow asparagus,
watch the tides
and listen to the
wind instead of
the politicians
make up your own
stories and believe
them if you want to
10   live the good life.

2
All rituals
are instincts
never fully
trust them
study to im-
prove biology
with reason.

3

Digging trenches
for asparagus
20   is good for the
muscles and
waiting for the
plants to settle
teaches patience
to those who are
usually in too
much of a hurry.

4

There is morality
in bee-keeping
30   it teaches how
not to be afraid
of the bee swarm
it teaches how
not to be afraid of
finding new places
and building them
all over again.

Warm Rain

by Midori Iwasaki

Warm
rain
runs
off fresh green boughs
and
wets
my
cheek

as I sail out
10   into
a
new
morning

1. **Response**
   a. What kind of a person is the speaker in "When I Heard the Learn'd Astronomer"? List at least three character traits with details from the poem that support your conclusions.
   b. Comment on the advice presented in "Advice to the Young." Does it seem useful or valuable to you? Explain.
   c. Reread "Warm Rain" and select the one word that you think is the most important or interesting. Explain your choice.

2. **Writing** *Poem* Each of the preceding three poems argues directly or indirectly in favour of direct experience with nature. Write a poem of your own, based on your personal experience, that makes the same point, or write a poem that refutes the other three poems. You can use one of these poems as a model, or choose another format.

Overwhelming Questions

Many poets explore, and may even answer, the overwhelming
questions that trouble us all—who or what am I? Is there a
purpose to life? What is the nature of happiness?

Original Thought

by The Four Dancers

Sometimes
it's hard
to raise a thought,
when you think
too hard,
thoughts create thinkers
or entangle non-thinkers
in chaos
with discordant rhymes,
10 thought takes the pen
and I wonder
sometimes
where thought even begins,
the norm think only in terms
of insanity
clustering pieces of thought
throughout their lives.

The luxury of unwrangling
stifled thought
may free the mind   20
allowing design
for creative communication,
silence,
one thought ebbs toward
        eternity,
threading the edge
of the thinker's mind
or
causing one to be fooled
by one's thought.   30
Thoughts captured in simplicity
hold glistening truths
to think
when the raising is hard.

Anything Worth Knowing?

by Kevin Major

In school that morning
he asked me, the teacher, what use it was for him
to know the parts of a worm
when his one use for worms was fishing.
I had no answer for him.
Except that some people want to know,
that the world is better for knowing.
If not him, then others were interested.

But that afternoon, after school
10   When he asked me, the learner, what use it was
for me to know the right way to bait a hook
("Your one use for worms is dissection")
I had an answer ready for him.
"Now I see that baiting hooks
destroys the crop, the gizzard, the dorsal ganglion!
Knowledge helps me understand the deadening of the
brain."

1. Response

a. With a small group, discuss the poem "Original Thought" and what the poet might have been trying to achieve or capture.

b. In a group, generate a list of effective strategies that would help readers to better understand a difficult poem such as "Original Thought." Present your conclusions to the class.

c. In "Anything Worth Knowing?" how does the teacher respond to the student's two questions? What do you think of the teacher's answers?

d. What essential question(s) does each poem ask? Is an answer provided?

2. Critical Thinking

Reflect on your own attitudes about learning. What kind of knowledge is most important to you? Which learning experiences have been most satisfying? Summarize your ideas in a brief piece of personal writing, and describe at least two learning goals you have for the future.

Did I Miss Anything?

by Tom Wayman

*Question frequently asked by students after
missing a class.*

Nothing. When we realized you weren't here
we sat with our hands folded on our desks
in silence, for the full two hours

    Everything. I gave an exam worth
    40 per cent of the grade for this term
    and assigned some reading due today
    on which I'm about to hand out a quiz
    worth 50 per cent

Nothing. None of the content of this course

10   has value or meaning
Take as many days off as you like:
any activities we undertake as a class
I assure you will not matter either to you or me
and are without purpose

    Everything. A few minutes after we began last time
    a shaft of light descended and an angel
    or other heavenly being appeared
    and revealed to us what each woman or man must do
    to attain divine wisdom in this life and

20   the hereafter
    This is the last time the class will meet
    before we disperse to bring this good news to all people
        on earth

Nothing. When you are not present
how could something significant occur?

    Everything. Contained in this classroom
    is a microcosm of human existence
    assembled for you to query and examine and ponder

    This is not the only place such an opportunity has been

30   gathered

    but it was one place

    and you weren't here

What Is the Validity of Your Life?

by Dorothy Livesay

The validity of my life
is a few poems caught and netted
a few strong feelings
about love and dying
and loss—
a few tempestuous cloudbursts
because people couldn't be
as great as they might have been
if they'd never learned
10   to play games—
a few doubts
about my own importance—
a delight   delighting in
puffed redbreast on a tree
eyeing me   and his mate
and the crows in the jack pine squawking
because there's a small grey cat
on the garage roof
spitting at them.

20   The validity of my life
is whether you read this poem
or not
and whether it speeds
your arrow.

1. Response

a. What audience do you think would most enjoy reading the poem "Did I Miss Anything?" Give reasons for your answer. What other audiences might enjoy the poem?

b. Describe the kinds of humour Wayman uses in "Did I Miss Anything?" In your own words, state the serious point he is arguing in his poem. Do you think his humorous approach is an effective way for him to express this point? Explain.

c. Discuss the image contained in the final two lines of "What Is the Validity of Your Life?" In your opinion, what meaning is the poet trying to convey through this image? How effectively does the image convey this meaning?

Afternoons and Coffeespoons

by Brad Roberts

What is it that makes me just a little bit queasy?
There's a breeze that makes my breathing not so easy
I've had my lungs checked out with X rays
I've smelled the hospital hallways

Someday I'll have a disappearing hairline
Someday I'll wear pyjamas in the daytime

Times when the day is like a play by Sartre
When it seems a bookburning's in perfect order—
I gave the doctor my description
10   I tried to stick to my prescriptions

Someday I'll have a disappearing hairline
Someday I'll wear pyjamas in the daytime

Afternoons will be measured out
Measured out, measured with
Coffeespoons and T. S. Eliot

Sartre: Jean-Paul Sartre (1905–1980), French novelist and philosopher

T. S. Eliot: Thomas Stearns Eliot (1888–1965), U.S.-born English poet, dramatist, and critic

Maybe if I could do a play-by-playback
I could change the test results that I will get back
I've watched the summer evenings pass by
I've heard the rattle in my bronchi ...
Someday I'll have a disappearing hairline
Someday I'll wear pyjamas in the daytime

Afternoons will be measured out
Measured out, measured with
20   Coffeespoons and T. S. Eliot

Old Man on Sea Shore, Saunton Sands, Devon by Bob Elsdale. Photo

What ideas about old age are communicated in this photo?
How specifically does the photo suggest those ideas? Gather
other images of older people from contemporary media works
and analyse them in the same way. Infer an audience and purpose
for each image. Draw at least two conclusions about social
attitudes toward aging, based on your analysis.

The Love Song of J. Alfred Prufrock

by T. S. Eliot

S'io credesse che mia risposta fosse
A persona che mai tornasse al mondo,
Questa fiamma staria senza più scosse.
Ma per cio che giammai di questo fondo
Non tornò viva alcun, s'i'odo il vero,
Senza tema d'infamia ti rispondo.[1]

Let us go then, you and I,
When the evening is spread out against the sky
Like a patient etherised[2] upon a table;
Let us go, through certain half-deserted streets,
The muttering retreats
Of restless nights in one-night cheap hotels
And sawdust restaurants[3] with oyster-shells:
Streets that follow like a tedious argument
Of insidious intent
10   To lead you to an overwhelming question …
Oh, do not ask, 'What is it?'
Let us go and make our visit.

    In the room the women come and go
Talking of Michelangelo.

    The yellow fog that rubs its back upon the window-panes,
The yellow smoke that rubs its muzzle on the window-panes
Licked its tongue into the corners of the evening,
Lingered upon the pools that stand in drains,
Let fall upon its back the soot that falls from chimneys,
20   Slipped by the terrace, made a sudden leap,
And seeing that it was a soft October night,
Curled once about the house, and fell asleep.

---

[1]**S'io credesse … ti rispondo:** "If I believed that my response [to your question about why such a respected person as myself is in Hell] was being addressed to a person who would soon return to the world, my tongue would cease to speak. However, since no one can ever leave these depths, if what I hear is true, I will answer your question, without fear of ruining my reputation." A quotation from Dante's *Inferno*.
[2]**etherised:** made unconscious by an anaesthetic
[3]**sawdust restaurants:** cheap restaurants with sawdust over a rough floor

And indeed there will be time
For the yellow smoke that slides along the street
Rubbing its back upon the window-panes;
There will be time, there will be time
To prepare a face to meet the faces that you meet;
There will be time to murder and create,
And time for all the works and days of hands
30   That lift and drop a question on your plate;
Time for you and time for me,
And time yet for a hundred indecisions,
And for a hundred visions and revisions,
Before the taking of a toast and tea.

In the room the women come and go
Talking of Michelangelo.

And indeed there will be time
To wonder, 'Do I dare?' and, 'Do I dare?'
Time to turn back and descend the stair,
40   With a bald spot in the middle of my hair—
(They will say: 'How his hair is growing thin!')
My morning coat, my collar mounting firmly to the chin,
My necktie rich and modest, but asserted by a simple pin—
(They will say: 'But how his arms and legs are thin!')
Do I dare
Disturb the universe?
In a minute there is time
For decisions and revisions which a minute will reverse.

For I have known them all already, known them all—
50   Have known the evenings, mornings, afternoons,
I have measured out my life with coffee spoons;
I know the voices dying with a dying fall
Beneath the music from a farther room.
   So how should I presume?

And I have known the eyes already, known them all—
The eyes that fix you in a formulated phrase,
And when I am formulated, sprawling on a pin,
When I am pinned and wriggling on the wall,
Then how should I begin
60   To spit out all the butt-ends of my days and ways?
   And how should I presume?

And I have known the arms already, known them all—
Arms that are braceleted and white and bare
(But in the lamplight, downed with light brown hair!)
Is it perfume from a dress
That makes me so digress?
Arms that lie along a table, or wrap about a shawl.
     And should I then presume?
     And how should I begin?

. . . . .

70   Shall I say, I have gone at dusk through narrow streets
And watched the smoke that rises from the pipes
Of lonely men in shirt-sleeves, leaning out of windows? ...

    I should have been a pair of ragged claws
Scuttling across the floors of silent seas.[4]

. . . . .

And the afternoon, the evening, sleeps so peacefully!
Smoothed by long fingers,
Asleep ... tired ... or it malingers,
Stretched on the floor, here beside you and me.
Should I, after tea and cakes and ices,
80   Have the strength to force the moment to its crisis?
But though I have wept and fasted, wept and prayed,
Though I have seen my head (grown slightly bald) brought in
      upon a platter,
I am no prophet—and here's no great matter;
I have seen the moment of my greatness flicker,
And I have seen the eternal Footman hold my coat, and snicker,
And in short, I was afraid.

    And would it have been worth it, after all,
After the cups, the marmalade, the tea,
90   Among the porcelain, among some talk of you and me,
Would it have been worth while,
To have bitten off the matter with a smile,
To have squeezed the universe into a ball
To roll it toward some overwhelming question,

---

[4] **ragged claws ... silent seas:** an allusion to remarks made by Shakespeare's Hamlet

To say: 'I am Lazarus,[5] come from the dead,
Come back to tell you all, I shall tell you all'—
If one, settling a pillow by her head,
    Should say: 'That is not what I meant at all.
    That is not it, at all.'

    And would it have been worth it, after all,
100 Would it have been worth while,
After the sunsets and the dooryards and the sprinkled streets,[6]
After the novels, after the teacups, after the skirts that trail
        along the floor—
And this, and so much more?—
It is impossible to say just what I mean!
But as if a magic lantern[7] threw the nerves in patterns on
        a screen:
Would it have been worth while
110 If one, settling a pillow or throwing off a shawl,
And turning toward the window, should say:
        'That is not it at all,
        That is not what I meant, at all.'

                    .   .   .   .   .

No! I am not Prince Hamlet, nor was meant to be;
Am an attendant lord, one that will do
To swell a progress, start a scene or two,
Advise the prince; no doubt, an easy tool,
Deferential, glad to be of use,
Politic, cautious, and meticulous;
120 Full of high sentence,[8] but a bit obtuse;
At times, indeed, almost ridiculous—
Almost, at times, the Fool.

        I grow old ... I grow old ...
I shall wear the bottoms of my trousers rolled.[9]

---

[5]**Lazarus:** In the Bible, Lazarus was brought back from the dead by Jesus.
[6]**sprinkled streets:** streets dampened with water to prevent dust
[7]**magic lantern:** a device used to project the image of a photograph onto a screen or wall
[8]**high sentence:** fine language used for serious ideas
[9]**the bottoms of my trousers rolled:** pants with cuffs (newly in fashion at the time)

Shall I part my hair behind? Do I dare to eat a peach?
I shall wear white flannel trousers, and walk upon the beach.
I have heard the mermaids singing, each to each.

I do not think that they will sing to me.

130

I have seen them riding seaward on the waves
Combing the white hair of the waves blown back
When the wind blows the water white and black.

We have lingered in the chambers of the sea
By sea-girls wreathed with seaweed red and brown
Till human voices wake us, and we drown.

Of our conflicts with others we make rhetoric;
of our conflicts with ourselves we make poetry.
—*William Butler Yeats*

Loneliness

by Emma LaRocque

Ah Loneliness,
How would I know
Who I am
Without you?

1. Response
   a. Write a complete character sketch for Prufrock. For each detail or trait in your sketch, provide supportive details from the poem.
   b. Do you think Prufrock ever reveals the nature of the "overwhelming question"? In a group, generate a list of overwhelming questions that a person like Prufrock might ask.
   c. Prufrock and the speaker in "Afternoons and Coffee-spoons" both speak of measuring out life "with coffee spoons." Write a brief explanation of what this metaphor suggests to you. In what way is the metaphor important to Eliot's poem and Roberts' song?
   d. According to the speaker in "Loneliness," what role does loneliness play in our lives? Would Prufrock be comfortable speaking the words in LaRocque's poem? Explain.

2. Research and Inquiry Using Internet or print resources, research the many allusions that T. S. Eliot includes in "The Love Song of J. Alfred Prufrock." Write a paragraph in which you reflect on whether researching the allusions helped you to better understand and/or appreciate the poem.

3. Making Connections Poets and other writers often use a quotation or line from someone else's work to inspire them or provide a context for their own creations. Choose a phrase or line from one of your favourite poems in this poetry unit and use it as a starting point for a poem of your own. Use the quotation you have borrowed as an introduction, as T. S. Eliot does, or incorporate it directly into your poem, as Roberts does.

Theme Connections

for all of the poems in the cluster "Overwhelming Questions"
- *"On the Rainy River," a story about personal values and choices, Vol. I, p. 70*
- *"The Spaces Between Stars," a story about values, Vol. I, p. 100*
- *"The Large Ant," a story about the human condition, Vol. I, p. 150*
- *"Living Like Weasels," an essay about the human condition, Vol. II, p. 106*
- *"What Will Your Verse Be?" a movie monologue about discovering who you are, Vol. II, p. 270*

Auto Wreck

by Karl Shapiro

Its quick soft silver bell beating, beating,
And down the dark one ruby flare
Pulsing out red light like an artery,
The ambulance at top speed floating down
Past beacons and illuminated clocks
Wings in a heavy curve, dips down,
And brakes speed, entering the crowd.
The doors leap open, emptying light;
Stretchers are laid out, the mangled lifted
10   And stowed into the little hospital.
Then the bell, breaking the hush, tolls once,
And the ambulance with its terrible cargo
Rocking, slightly rocking, moves away,
As the doors, an afterthought, are closed.

We are deranged, walking among the cops
Who sweep glass and are large and composed.
One is still making notes under the light.
One with a bucket douches ponds of blood
Into the street and gutter.
20   One hangs lanterns on the wrecks that cling,
Empty husks of locusts, to iron poles.

Our throats were tight as tourniquets,
Our feet were bound with splints, but now,
Like convalescents intimate and gauche,
We speak through sickly smiles and warn
With the stubborn saw of common sense,
The grim joke and the banal resolution.
The traffic moves around with care,
But we remain, touching a wound
30   That opens to our richest horror.

Already old, the question Who shall die?
Becomes unspoken Who is innocent?
For death in war is done by hands;

Suicide has cause and stillbirth, logic;
And cancer, simple as a flower, blooms.
But this invites the occult mind,
Cancels our physics with a sneer,
And spatters all we knew of denouement
Across the expedient and wicked stones.

Provisions

by Margaret Atwood

What should we have taken
with us? We never could decide
on that; or what to wear,
or at what time of
year we should make this journey

so here we are, in thin
raincoats and rubber boots

on the disastrous ice, the wind rising,

nothing in our pockets

10   but a pencil stub, two oranges
four toronto streetcar tickets

and an elastic band, holding a bundle
of small white filing-cards
printed with important facts.

1. Response

a. Why do you think Karl Shapiro, in his poem "Auto Wreck," describes the accident scene in such detail? Which details made the strongest impact on you? Explain.

b. What does the word *provisions* mean, and what connotations and associations does it carry for you? Use this information to comment on how the title shapes the meaning of Atwood's poem?

2. Literature Studies *Analysis*

In a group, discuss and analyse "Auto Wreck" and "Provisions." For each poem, describe its literal and symbolic subject matter. What overwhelming question(s) is posed in each poem? Are any answers supplied, either directly or indirectly? As a final task, record the different personal reactions your group members had to these two works, and assess their effectiveness.

3. Language Conventions *Descriptive Language*

Create a chart with the following headings: Nouns, Adjectives, Verbs, and **Verbals**. Use the chart to explore the descriptive language in "Auto Wreck," categorizing all the words in the poem that you think are unusual or especially well chosen. Explain what you learned about the poem by completing your chart.

Verbals look like verbs but function as other parts of speech. There are three kinds of verbals: infinitives, participles, and gerunds.

4. Film Study

Many feature films contain protagonists who are faced with overwhelming questions relating to personal identity and one's place in the world. In a group, make a list of recent films that contain such a character. For each film, describe what questions of identity the character faced and explore how those questions were (or were not) resolved. Based on your discussion, are there any general observations you can make about the way our culture regards the quest for identity?

> Poetry is the most direct and simple means of expressing oneself in words … If you listen to small children, and to the amount of chanting and singsong in their speech, you'll see what I mean.
>
> —*Northrop Frye*

Circular Saws

by Fred Cogswell

When the circular saw
chewed up my fingernail
I said to myself
"This is a bad dream
and I shall wake up"
but I didn't
and in a few minutes
the pain began

after that, I had
10   a scar to remind me
not to go near
circular saws

But I soon found
they had ways
of disguising themselves
so that watch as I might
they were always
hurting me

now inside and out
20   I am covered with scars
but that is not
the worst I've learned
the worst thing is
that under the masks
I wear and without
intending to be
I am a circular saw

Night

by Yvonne Trainer

I was never afraid of the night
I'd sit on the farmhouse step and watch the stars
I'd count 5 up from the Big Dipper
to find the smaller one
the one with the bent handle
that leaked rain

I remember the white enamel dipper
that hung on a nail above the washstand
My Mother polishing it once a day

10 My Father chipping it when he threw it against the wall
in anger over something   I've forgotten
It doesn't matter

Still   light from the window
casts shadows over the yard
but the sky is calm
A whole universe
and nobody throws the stars
Everything has its place
        has order

20 Even the spaces belong.

Response

a. Which poem, "Circular Saws" or "Night," had the strongest impact on you after the first reading? Briefly explain why you think this was the case.

b. Reread "Night" carefully and then offer an interpretation of this particular phrase from the poem: "and nobody throws the stars."

c. Sometimes the questions a poem raises are implicit rather than explicit. What do you think the implicit questions are in "Circular Saws" and "Night"?

Poet Biographies

MARISA ANLIN ALPS graduated from Simon Fraser University and now works in the publishing industry. Her poetry is included in the collection *Breathing Fire: Canada's New Poets* and has also been broadcast on CBC radio.

MATTHEW ARNOLD (1822–88) was born in Laleham, England. He is best known as a poet but was also an influential critic, educator, and professor.

MARGARET AVISON was born in 1918 in Galt, Ontario. She lived as a child in Regina and Calgary, then returned to Ontario to go to school at the University of Toronto. Her poetry anthologies include *No time, Not Yet but Still, Winter Sun/The Dumbfounding: poems, 1940–66*, and *sunblue*.

AMIRI BARAKA (born LeRoi Jones in 1934) is a poet, activist, social critic, dramatist, and fiction writer. His work and life show his development through social discovery and rebellion, as well as a clear response to the injustice he faced every day.

RICHARD BRAUTIGAN was born in Tacoma, Washington in 1935. He was part of the Beat Movement during the fifties. His books include *The Hawkline Monster: a gothic western, Willard and His Bowling Trophies: A Perverse Mystery, Trout Fishing in America*, and *Revenge of the Lawn*.

ELIZABETH BREWSTER was born in New Brunswick in 1922. She has won numerous awards for her poetry, including the President's Silver Medal for Poetry and the Saskatchewan Arts Boards' Lifetime Award for Excellence in the Arts.

ELIZABETH BARRETT BROWNING was born in England in 1806. Her first poetry collection, *An Essay on Mind and Other Poems*, was published anonymously. In 1844, her collection, *Poems*, gained the attention of the poet Robert Browning. They eloped in 1846. Barrett's *Sonnets From the Portuguese*, dedicated to her husband, was published in 1850, and her verse novel, *Aurora Leigh*, in 1857.

ROBERT BROWNING, born in England in 1812, was a less recognized poet than his wife, Elizabeth Barrett Browning, during their lifetime. However, as a poet, he was considered famous enough to be buried in London's Westminster Abbey among the greatest figures in British history, following his death in 1889.

MARILYN CAY lives in Tisdale, Saskatchewan. She writes poetry and nonfiction and has published two books— *Farm* and *Pure and Startled Seconds*.

FRED COGSWELL, born in East Centreville, New Brunswick in 1917, was the editor of *The Fiddlehead* and two volumes of East Coast writing. He has won many awards, including the Bliss Carman Award for Poetry. His written works include *Watching an Eagle, As I See It*, and *In My Own Growing*.

LORNA CROZIER, along with other Saskatchewan writers, founded a monthly writing workshop jokingly named *The Moose Jaw Movement*. In 1992, her poetry collection, *Inventing the Hawk*, won the Governor General's Award.

EDWARD ESTLIN CUMMINGS is known as an experimental poet. Although his name often appears without capitalization, this was never at the legal request, or even wish, of Cummings himself. It was one publisher's style decision, which was adopted by subsequent publishers as the "correct" style.

EDWARD DE VERE, the 17th Earl of Oxford, was born in 1550 in Castle Heddingham in Essex, England. He acted and produced plays, as part of a court circle of writers. He died in 1604. The debate still rages over whether he was the author of Shakespeare's plays.

EMILY DICKINSON, born in 1830, remained in almost total physical isolation from the outside world most of her life. She was an extremely prolific poet, but was not publicly recognized during her lifetime. She died in 1886.

JOHN W. DICKSON was a Harvard professor, poet, and dramatist. He won the Pulitzer Prize for poetry.

THOMAS STEARNS ELIOT was born in Missouri in 1888, but settled in England in 1914. His first book of poems—*Prufrock and Other Observations*—immediately established him as a leading poet. He received the Nobel Prize for Literature in 1948, and died in London in 1965.

MARI EVANS, born in 1923 in Toledo Ohio, was raised in a very traditional African American home. She wrote, produced, and directed the TV program *The Black Experience*, the play *River of My Song*, the musical *Eyes*, and the poetry collections *Nightstar* and *A Dark and Splendid Mass*.

THE FOUR DANCERS are H. Bear Bones, J.C. Rippling Water, Ola Hummingbird, and G. Walking in the Sky.

ROBERT FROST was born in San Francisco in 1874. His first two poetry collections—*A Boy's Will* and *North of Boston*—established his reputation as a poet. His later poetry collections won him more fame and honours, including four Pulitzer Prizes. He died in Boston in 1963.

NIKKI GIOVANNI is a writer of prose and of adult and children's poetry, and is also well known for her poetry recitals. She has received many awards for her written and performed poetry.

PHYLLIS GOTLIEB was born Phyllis Bloom in Toronto in 1926. Her books include the poetry collections *Within the Zodiac* and *Doctor UmLaut's Earthly Kingdom*; the science fiction novels *Sunburst*, *The Kingdom of the Cats*, *Flesh and Gold*, and *Violent Stars*; and the story anthologies *Son of the Morning and Other Stories* and *Blue Apes*. She has also written verse plays for the CBC.

RICK HILLIS wrote *The Blue Machines of Night* and *Limbo River*. He is a professor at Reed College in Portland, Oregon, currently teaching poetry, fiction, and screenwriting.

MARIA HOLOD was born in 1917 in Lviv, Western Ukraine. She graduated from the University of Lviv, then emigrated to Canada in 1948. Her writing has appeared in various anthologies and journals, and her book, *Chotyry pory roku (The four seasons)*, was published in 1978.

LENORE KEESHIG-TOBIAS has been a storyteller since she was a child; the oldest of ten children, she would amuse her younger brothers and sisters with stories. Keeshig-Tobias teaches oral studies at George Brown College in Toronto. She is interested in the oral traditions of all cultures, and has founded a society to preserve stories of the Trickster.

STANLEY KUNITZ was born in 1905 in Massachusetts. He went to school at Harvard where he received the Garrison Medal for Poetry. He wrote his first book of poems, *Intellectual Things*, before he was twenty-five. He won the Pulitzer Prize in 1959 for *Selected Poems: 1928–1958*. His work has been described as "combining a classical strength of language and vision which goes beyond the easier uses of irony and achieves the genuinely tragic." He is an active member of civil liberty and peace organizations.

ARCHIBALD LAMPMAN, born in 1861, in Morpeth, Canada West (a village near what is now Chatham, Ontario), attended Trinity College in Toronto, worked unsuccessfully as a teacher, but with greater success as a clerk in the post office in Ottawa—a post he held until his death in 1899. He was a writer of poetry, literary essays, and articles. He was one of the Confederation Writers, a group of poets that included Bliss Carman, Susanna Moodie, Charles G. D. Roberts, and Duncan Campbell Scott. His works include *Among the Millet, and Other Poems*, and *Lyrics of Earth*.

EMMA LaROCQUE is an expert on colonization and its impact on Aboriginal/White relations. She wrote *Defeathering the Indian* and many articles about Aboriginal literature, racism, and violence against women. Vicki Gaboreau and Peter Gzowski have both had her as a guest on their programs.

DOROTHY LIVESAY (1909–1996) was born in Winnipeg, Manitoba. She worked as a teacher from 1959 to 1963 in Northern Rhodesia (Zambia). She won the Governor General's Literary Award twice; in 1944 for *Day and Night*, and in 1947 for *Poems for People*.

VALERIO MAGRELLI was born in 1957 in Rome. Described as a post-modern or post-atomic poet, he wrote the poetry collection *The Contagion of Matter.*

KEVIN MAJOR, an important figure in Canadian young-adult literature, lives and writes in St. John's, Newfoundland and Labrador.

Born in 1564, CHRISTOPHER MARLOWE (the son of a shoemaker) had a brilliant but short career, with violence, heresy, and sedition playing a role. Marlowe was an innovative, intellectual thinker, writing the plays *Tamburlaine, Dr. Faustus, The Jew of Malta*, and *Edward II*. In 1593, Marlowe pointed out what he thought were inconsistencies in the Bible. On May 30 of that year, he was murdered at Bull's Tavern over an argument about the bill. Debate rages over whether Marlowe was deliberately provoked and murdered to prevent him revealing the names of fellow heretics, if arrested.

EDNA ST. VINCENT MILLAY, born in 1892, was a poet and playwright. In 1923, her fourth volume of poems, *The Harp Weaver*, was awarded the Pulitzer Prize.

As a young student, JONI MITCHELL thought she would be an artist; it was only as she became exposed to other musicians through the sixties that she began to turn to music, especially songwriting, as a career. She has produced more than twenty albums and is recognized as one of the most significant and consistent contributors of her generation. Her music often incorporates several styles and is hard to classify but is always captivating.

PAUL MULDOON was born in Ireland in 1951. He began writing poetry in Irish at the age of seventeen. His first volume of poetry, *New Weather*, was published in 1973 while he was still at university. After grad-uation he worked as a radio and TV producer for the BBC. He lives in the United States, and his poetry anthologies have won various awards.

OGDEN NASH was born in New York in 1902. He published his first book for children, *The Cricket of Caradon*, in 1925, and his first poem appeared in *The New Yorker* in 1932. Nash published nineteen books of poetry throughout his lifetime and is probably best known for his limericks.

MARGE PIERCY, born in 1936 in Detroit, Michigan, almost died from German measles and rheumatic fever as a child. She took refuge from illness in stories and books. She supported herself after college by working part-time at a number of jobs—secretary, clerk, faculty instructor, switchboard operator—while trying to write and publish poetry and fiction. She wrote the novels *Going Down Fast* and *Dance the Eagle to Sleep* while actively opposing American involvement in the Vietnam war.

ROBERT PINSKY'S (American Poet Laureate) poetry collections include *Jersey Rain, Sadness and Happiness, The Figured Wheel*, and *New and Collected Poems, 1966–1996*; he also wrote the non-fiction book *The Sounds of Poetry: A Brief Guide.*

KATHLEEN RAINE is a poet, scholar, and critic. She has won the Edna St. Vincent Millay Prize from the American Poetry Society, and the Harriet Monroe Prize. She lives in London, England. Her poetry is described as "a kind of mystical nature poetry … immersed in the quiet air of solitude and imagination."

SIR WALTER RALEIGH is better known as an explorer, soldier, pirate, and adventurer than a poet. He was born in 1552 (some reports say 1554), in Devon. Raleigh fought with the French Huguenots in 1569. Then, with a half brother, Sir Humphrey Gilbert, he fought the Spanish at sea—an act of piracy that won him the favour of Queen Elizabeth I. He was sent to Ireland to suppress rebellion, which he did ruthlessly, and returned to London and the royal court still in favour. Expeditions he funded returned from Virginia (the "new world") with potatoes and tobacco. His star rose and fell during the years that followed. Unfortunately, on the queen's death, King James gained the throne and Raleigh was accused of treason and confined to the Tower of London (a prison) where he remained for thirteen years (writing his history of the world). In 1616, he was released to again mount an expedition to the "new world." On his return in 1618, Raleigh was executed.

Singer-songwriter BRAD ROBERTS is the lead vocalist of the Canadian rock group Crash Test Dummies. Roberts grew up in Winnipeg. In 1990, while still in university, he formed the Crash Test Dummies together with his brother, bassist Dan Roberts, and three friends. Roberts also performs as a soloist.

GERALDINE RUBIA, born in 1929 in Brooklyn, New York, now lives in Newfoundland and Labrador. She has written for radio, TV, and theatre.

WILLIAM SHAKESPEARE was born in 1564, in Stratford-on-Avon, England. He composed over a hundred sonnets between 1593 and 1601. These were written in the form of three quatrains and a rhyming couplet, now recognized as the Shakespearean sonnet. He died in 1616.

KARL SHAPIRO, born in 1913, began writing poetry while young. While serving in the army during WWII, the poems that he sent home to his fiancée were published. He returned from the war to find that he was a popular poet and he remained so, despite his stance against the poetic conventions and theories of the time.

TSUBOI SHIGEJI was born in 1889 in Japan. He wrote about the problems besetting the poor workers—and these views and writing led to his imprisonment.

PAUL SIMON grew up in the suburbs of New York City. His successful career as a singer and songwriter has spanned several decades. Simon is as acclaimed for his many enduring songs as he is for his musical innovations. Once part of folk-rock group Simon and Garfunkel, he has recorded many award-winning solo albums and has written music for films and stage.

DYLAN THOMAS was born in Wales in 1914. Although he excelled in English and reading, he dropped out of school when he was sixteen. His first book—*Eighteen Poems*—was published to great acclaim when he was twenty. He died in 1953 at the age of thirty-nine.

MIRIAM WADDINGTON was born in Winnipeg in 1917. She was the Canada Council Exchange Poet to Wales in 1980, and has been poetry editor of *Poetry Toronto*, and writer-in-residence at both the Windsor Public Library and the University of Ottawa.

TOM WAYMAN, born in Ontario in 1945, moved to Prince Rupert, British Columbia as a child, and then moved again, to Vancouver, when he was fourteen. He has written and published poetry collections, including *Paperwork, Did I Miss Anything?* and *The Astonishing Weight of the Dead*. He also writes essays and plays, and edits anthologies.

WALT WHITMAN is one of the most famous American poets of the nineteenth century. Born in 1819 in New York City, Whitman was a brilliant child and a voracious reader. He worked as a printer, teacher, journalist, and nurse, and cared deeply for the victims of war and slavery. His first and most popular book is *Leaves of Grass*. Whitman died in 1892.

WILLIAM WORDSWORTH was born in 1770 in England. Wordsworth's earliest poetry collections—*An Evening Walk* and *Descriptive Sketches*—were published in 1793. He died in 1850 and his most famous poem, *"The Prelude,"* was published posthumously by his wife.

Glossary

In the **active voice**, the subject of a sentence does the action. For example, *The dog ran into the street*. Use the active voice when possible. It uses fewer words and is more precise than the passive voice. See **passive voice**.

An **allegory** is a simple story, such as a fable or parable, whose major purpose is to teach a moral lesson. An allegory can always be read on two levels—one literal, the other symbolic. The underlying meaning can be parallel to, but different from, the surface meaning.

Alliteration is a repetition of the same first sound in a group of words or line of poetry. For example, *The sun sank slowly*.

An **allusion**, in a literary work, is a reference to another literary work, or a person, place, event, or object from history, literature, or mythology. For example, *If you take the last piece of pie, you can expect WW II all over again*.

An **analogy** is the illustration of one idea or concept by using a similar idea or concept. An analogy can be phrased as a simile.

The **antagonist** of a narrative or dramatic work is the primary person in opposition to the hero or **protagonist**.

Apposition is the relation of two parts of a sentence when the one is added as an explanation to the other. For example, in *Mr. Brown, our teacher, is on vacation, Mr. Brown* and *teacher* are in apposition.

An **archetype** is a theme, symbol, character, or setting that can be found throughout literature, folklore, and media so often that it comes to reflect some universal human character or experience. For example, *Robin Hood* is an archetypal hero.

Assonance (also known as *vowel rhyme*) is the repetition of similar or identical vowel sounds within the words of a poem or other writing. For example, *mellow wedding bells*.

Bias is the author's inclination or preference toward one stance that makes it difficult or impossible to judge something fairly. For example, *a Sylvester Stallone fan may be unable to write an objective or balanced review of Stallone's work*.

A **burlesque** is a literary or dramatic composition in which a serious subject is treated ridiculously or with mock seriousness.

A **cacophony** is a harsh or clashing combination of words, often caused deliberately for effect. For example, finger of a *birth-strangled* babe.

A **caesura** is a pause in a line of verse, generally agreeing with a pause required by the sense. For example, *England — how I long for thee!*

Climax See **plot.**

Closure occurs when a story ends without ambiguity. The main crises and/or conflicts are neatly wrapped up, and the reader has a sense that the story is truly finished. In an *open-ended story,* the reader is uncertain about what might happen next; several outcomes are possible.

Codes and **conventions** refer to the different ways in which each media product typically conveys meaning to audiences. For example, we expect certain kinds of movies to open with certain conventions, such as an action movie opening with lots of action, special effects, and maybe a chase scene.

Consonance is the repetition of similar or identical consonants in words whose vowels differ. For example, *gripe, grape, grope.*

Diction refers to the way an author expresses ideas in words. Good diction includes grammatical correctness, skill in the choice of effective words, and a wide vocabulary.

A **dynamic character** is one who undergoes a significant and permanent change in personality or beliefs.

Enjambment occurs when there is no strong punctuation at the end of a line of poetry, allowing a phrase or sentence to carry through that line and into the next without a pause. For example,

> *Let me not to the marriage of true minds*
> *Admit impediments. Love is not love*
> —Shakespeare

A **eulogy** is a tribute to someone who has just died and is often delivered as a speech at a funeral.

A **fact sheet** presents key information about a particular topic, issue, or organization. It provides concise answers to basic questions. Some fact sheets are written in point form, others in full sentences.

Figurative language uses words to paint a picture, draw an interesting comparison, or create a poetic effect. **Literal language** says what it means directly. Language can be figurative or literal.

Free-verse poetry is written without using regular rhyme or rhythm. Images, spacing, punctuation, and the rhythms of ordinary language are used to create a free-verse poem.

Foreshadowing is a plot technique in which a writer plants clues or subtle indications about events that will happen later in the narrative.

Imagery is the pictures or impressions that writers create in the minds of their readers. To create these pictures, they use descriptive techniques such as figures of speech (simile, metaphor, personification, oxymoron), onomatopoeia, alliteration, and allusions.

Irony occurs when a statement or situation means something different from (or even the opposite of) what is expected. Another type of irony is called **dramatic irony**. It occurs in plays when the audience knows something that the characters do not.

Interjections are words—such as *oh, wow, ha, mmm*—that show emotion, often without any grammatical connection to other parts of the sentence.

Juxtaposition is the intentional placement of dissimilar words or ideas side by side for a particular purpose—to emphasize contrasting ideas, for example.

A **literary essay** presents an interpretation or explores some aspect of one or more works of literature.

Loaded language is language that is intentionally chosen to evoke a strong response in a reader—usually an emotional response. It is also language that is highly connotative, conjuring in the listener much more than its literal meaning.

A **loaded word** is a word intentionally chosen to evoke a strong response in a reader—usually an emotional response.

A **logo** is an identifying symbol used as a trademark in advertising.

Mass media is any method by which a message is communicated to a large audience at the same time—*movies, radio, TV, books, magazines, the Internet.*

A **media text** is any media product—*movie, radio show, CD, TV program,* et cetera—that is selected for critical examination.

A **metaphor** is a comparison of two things that are not alike. The comparison suggests that they do share a common quality: *His words were a knife to my heart.*

An **oxymoron** is a figure of speech that is a combination of contradictory words. One of the most common examples of an oxymoron is *jumbo shrimp.*

Parallelism is the intentional use of identical or similar grammatical structure within one sentence or in two or more sentences. For example, *She likes dancing, singing, and jogging.*

Parallel structure is the repeated use of the same phrase or sentence, or the repeated use of a similar sentence structure. Parallel structure can be used to create balance or place emphasis on certain lines.

In the **passive voice**, the subject of the verb receives the action: *The fire was extinguished.* See **Active Voice**.

The **persona** is the voice or character that represents the narrator in a literary work. A persona is often described as a mask an author deliberately puts on in order to narrate a particular story or poem.

Personification occurs when objects, ideas, or animals are given human qualities: *The sun smiled down on me.*

Plot refers to the events in a story. Plot usually has five elements: exposition, rising action, climax, falling action, and resolution.
- The **exposition** or introduction sets up the story by introducing the main characters, the setting, and the problem to be solved.
- The **rising action** is the main part of the story where the full problem develops. A number of events is involved that will lead to the climax.
- The **climax** is the highest point in the story where something decisive occurs.
- The **falling action** follows the climax. It contains the events that bring the story to its conclusion.
- The **resolution** or denouement is the end of the story and traces the final outcome of the central conflict.

A **point of view** is the vantage point from which the author tells a story. The four most common points of view are *first person* (I, me), *omniscient* (all seeing), *limited omniscient* (all seeing from the viewpoint of a group of characters), and *objective* (he, she, they, it).

A **précis** is a concise summary of a text. It is written in full sentences, but contains only the most important information.

A **process analysis** shows how something is done. It gives information about a process, usually in the same order as the process itself.

A **proverb** is a short saying that expresses a basic truth or useful principle. For example, *Look before you leap.*

Racist language is any language that refers to a particular cultural group or ethnic group in insulting terms, but racism also exists in more subtle forms. To avoid even subtle racism, remember the following:

- Mention a person's race only if it is relevant to the context. If a person's race or ethnic origin is relevant, be specific:
  Irrelevant/Vague: *Dago is African.*
  Relevant/Less Vague: *Dago is proud of her Nigerian heritage.*
- Avoid making generalizations about any racial or cultural group:
  Stereotype: *The Welsh are great singers.*
  Better: *The Welsh have a long tradition of singing.*

Register refers to the level of formality of language. Language can be characterized according to the social context for which it is appropriate. For example, language with a colloquial register might contain slang expressions and unconventional grammar.

Resolution See **plot**.

A **rhetorical question** is one that is asked for effect, and that does not invite a reply. The purpose of a rhetorical question is to introduce a topic or to focus the reader on a concern. For example, *How do I love thee? Let me count the ways.*

Rhythm is the arrangement of beats in a line of poetry. The beat is created by the accented and unaccented syllables in the words used in each line.

A **satire** is a work that criticizes something—for example, *a person, a characteristic, an institution, or a government*—by depicting it in a humorous, sarcastic, or scornful way.

Sexist language is language that degrades or unnecessarily excludes either women or men. It is best to avoid generalizing about males and females unless the claims are based on scientific facts. To avoid sexist language, remember the following:

- Whenever possible, replace words such as *fireman, policeman,* and *man-made* with non-sexist alternatives such as *firefighter, police officer,* and *fabricated.*
- Avoid using the masculine pronouns *he, him,* or *his* to refer to both men and women.
  Sexist: A doctor must always be polite to his patients.
  Non-sexist: Doctors must always be polite to their patients. **OR**
                  A Doctor must always be polite to his/her patients.

A **stereotype** is an oversimplified picture, usually of a group of people, giving them all a set of characteristics, without consideration for individual differences. For example, *the nerd scientist, the rebellious teenager,* and *the bratty younger brother* are all stereotypes.

Style is the overall texture of a piece of writing; the particular way in which the ideas are expressed. Style is made up of many elements including diction, figurative language, sentences, and tone.

Suspense is a feeling of tension, anxiety, or excitement resulting from uncertainty. An author creates suspense to keep readers interested.

A **symbol** is something that represents something else—for example, *the lion can be a symbol of courage.*

The **symbolic meaning** of a work is developed through the symbols that the author includes.

A **synopsis** provides an overview or summary of a longer work.

A **theme** is a central thesis or idea that is expressed directly or indirectly in a literary work.

The **thesis** of an essay is the main idea or argument that the author is attempting to prove.

Tone is the implied attitude of the writer toward the subject or the audience. Tone differs from mood, which describes the emotional feeling of the work more generally. The tone of a piece of work can be described, for example, as *angry, satiric, joyful,* or *serious.*

Transition words—such as *however, in conclusion,* and *on the other hand*—indicate relationships between ideas. Writers use them to suggest links between sentences or paragraphs.

A **unifying device** connects different parts of a narrative. It can be a metaphor, a symbol, an image, a character, or even an important word or phrase.

Verbals look like verbs but function as other parts of speech. There are three kinds of verbals: infinitives, participles, and gerunds. An infinitive can function as a noun, adjective, or adverb, and takes the form of a verb preceded by "to": *I'll continue to hope for good weather.* A participle functions as an adjective and takes the form of a verb + "ing" (present participle) or "ed" (past participle): *I am hoping for good weather. I hoped for good weather.* A gerund functions as a noun and takes the form of a verb + "ing": *Hoping is something I do all the time.*

Index of Titles and Authors

Index of Artists and Images

Acknowledgments

Every reasonable effort has been made to trace ownership of copyrighted material. Information that would enable the publisher to correct any reference or credit in future editions would be appreciated.

12 "Groom Service" from *Working Men* by Michael Dorris, © 1993 by Michael Dorris. Reprinted by permission of Henry Holt and Company, LLC. 44 "The Return" by Ngugi Wa Thiong'o from *Secrets Lives and Other Stories* by Ngugi Wa Thiong'o. Reprinted by permission of Heinemann Educational Publishers. 51 "Two Words" by Isabel Allende. Reprinted with the permission of Scribner, a Division of Simon & Schuster, Inc., from *The Stories of Eva Luna* by Isabel Allende, translated by Margaret Sayers Peden. © 1989 by Isabel Allende. English translation, © 1991 by Macmillan Publishing Company. 60 "A Marker on the Side of the Boat" by Boa Ninh. Originally published in the magazine *Tap Chi Van Nghe Quan Doi*, 1994. Published here in English by the permission of the author. Translation © 1990 by Linh Dinh. 70 "On a Rainy River" from *The Things They Carried* by Tim O'Brien. © 1990 by Tim O'Brien. Reprinted by permission of Houghton Mifflin Company. All rights reserved. 86 "A Pair of Silk Stockings", from The Awakening and Selected Stories by Kate Chopin, Introduction by Barbara H. Soloman, © 1976 by The New American Library, Inc., Introduction. Used by permission of Dutton Signet, a division of Penguin Putnam Inc. 92 "Dressing Up for the Carnival" by Carol Shields. Extracted from *Dressing Up for the Carnival* by Carol Shields. © 2000 by Carol Shields. Reprinted by permission of Random House Canada, a division of Random House of Canada Limited. 100 "The Spaces Between Stars" by Geeta Kothari. Reprinted by permission of the author. 112 "The Chrysanthemums" by John Steinbeck, © 1937, renewed © 1965 by John Steinbeck. from *The Long Valley* by John Steinbeck. Used by permission of Viking Penguin, a division of Penguin Putnam Inc. 124 "Touching Bottom" by Kari Stutt. Reprinted by permission of the author. 134 "The Forest of Arden" by Hannah Grant. Reprinted by permission of the author. 143 "Things That Fly" by Douglas Coupland. Reprinted with the permission of Simon & Schuster from *Life After God* by Douglas Coupland. © 1994 by Douglas Coupland. 150 "The Large Ant" by Howard Fast. Reprinted by permission of Sterling Lord Literistic, Inc. © by Howard Fast. 160 "A Drowning" from *Hearts Larry Broke* by Mark Ferguson (published by Creative Book Publishing). Reprinted by permission of the author. 164 "Red Bean Ice" by Nancy Lee. Reprinted

by permission of the author. 174 "If a Poem Could Walk" from *Angels of Flesh, Angels of Silence* by Lorna Crozier. Used by permission of the Canadian Publishers, McClelland & Stewart, Toronto. 177 "After the Wedding" by Marisa Anlin Alps. Reprinted with permission of the author. 178 "Brian at Eighteen" from *The Blue Machines of Night* by Rick Hillis (Coteau Books, 1988). Reprinted by permission from the author. 182 "Pride" by Marilyn Cay from *Farm* (Thistledown Press, 1993). 183 "Silent, but…" by Tsuboi Sheigeji from *The Penguin Book of Japanese Verse* translated by Geoffrey Bownas and Anthony Thwaite. Reprinted by permission of Penguin Books Ltd. London: Penguin Books. 1964 184 "On the Value of Fantasies" by Elizabeth Brewster. Reprinted from *Sometimes I Think of Moving* by Permission of Oberon Press. 186 "The Swimmer's Moment" from *Winter Sun/The Dumbfounding Poems 1940-1966* by Margaret Avison. Used by permission of McClelland & Stewart Ltd. The Canadian Publishers. 186 "Symposium" from *Hay* by Paul Muldoon. © 1998 by Paul Muldoon. Reprinted by permission of Farrar, Straus, and Giroux, LLC. 188 "The Layers" by Stanley Kunitz. Reprinted by permission of the author. 189 "Young Soul" by Amiri Baraka. Reprinted by permission of the author. 191 "Since Feeling Is First" © 1926, 1954, 1991 from *Collected Poems 1904-1962* by E.E. Cummings. Used by permission of Liverlight Publishing Corporation. 192 "Love Is Not All" by Edna St. Vincent Millay. From *Collected Poems*, HarperCollins. © 1931, 1958 by Edna St. Vincent Millay and Norma Millay Ellis. All rights reserved. Used by permission of Elizabeth Barnett, literary executor. 194 "I Wish to Paint My Eyes" 6 lines, by Anonymous, Trans. By Willis Barnstone, from *A Book of Women Poets from Antiquity to Now* by Willis Barnstone and Aliki Barnstone, © 1980 by Schocken Books. Used by permission of Schocken Books, a division of Random House, Inc. 200 "Variations on the Word *Love*" from *Selected Poems 1966-1984* by Margaret Atwood © Margaret Atwood 1990. Reprinted by permission of Oxford University Press Canada. 202 "First Person Demonstrative" by Phyllis Gotlieb. Reprinted by permission of the author. 207 "The Chariot (Because I Could Not Stop for Death)" by Emily Dickinson. Reprinted by permission of the publishers and the Trustees of Amherst College from *The Poems of Emily Dickinson*, Thomas H. Johnson, ed,. Cambridge, Mass.: The Belknap Press of Harvard University Press, © 1951, 1955, 1979 by the President and Fellows of Harvard College. 208 "Miss Dickinson Goes to the Office." Reprinted with permission of the author. 209 "Do Not Go